Nylon Kid

of the North

Also by Philip Paris

The Italian Chapel

Orkney's Italian Chapel: The True Story of an Icon

Trouble Shooting for Printers

Nylon Kid

of the North

To Denis

Best Wishes

Philip Paris

11th June 2012

Philip Paris

First published 2012
By Philip Paris
The Churchbell House, Fearn, Tain IV20 1WN.

ISBN: 978-0-9572356-0-1

A catalogue record for this book is available from the
British Library.

Photography by Robert Paris
Cover design by William Palmer
Printed and bound in the UK by the MPG Books Group,
Bodmin and King's Lynn.

Acknowledgements

Iain, Madeleine, Phyllis, Steve and Wendy for proof-reading early drafts, Gale for her professional book editing skills, William for cover design, AJ for his much appreciated computer knowledge, and to my wife Catherine for her love, support and encouragement.

To Mam, who died in 2010 of pancreatic
cancer at the age of eighty-six.

Chapter One

I stopped. The two men chasing me had caught up. They were strangers; young, earnest ... and eager to save me. One laid a hand gently on my arm.

'Come back inside,' he said.

'Inside' was a school hall where some 200 people sat in stunned silence, watching intently the scene played out before them, through the glass that made up most of that part of the building. Just my luck. I could see them out of the corner of my eye and imagined every one praying for my soul with great fervour. The only noise was the crunching of feet on gravel. Feet had rarely sounded so *angry*. I turned my head towards the source.

Babs, handbag clutched tightly to her tweed-covered bosom, strode towards her car, an unstoppable force of irritation and indignation. I noticed no one chased after her. Nobody tried to prevent her from leaving. God help them if they dared. Actually, it was God, or rather one interpretation of how to worship Him, which had caused this conflict.

'Someone else will take you home,' said the man, his hand still making contact with my elbow.

He was in his early twenties, the same as me. I had been in the hall for about an hour when Babs had exploded. Standing up suddenly, she had barged her way along the row, several people having to sit down with a rather undignified bump, when they had jumped up to praise the Lord at the wrong moment.

But to explain the scene, I have to return to events that had taken place prior to this Sunday morning towards the end of May, in 1981. I had arrived at Watford College the previous September and met Babs at the local folk dance group, which was held every Monday evening at Christ Church hall. She must have been around sixty, pretty much the average of the class. There was only one other person near my age, a girl named Rose, so we generally danced together and were good friends.

During one interval, while we munched on slices of Bertha's bread-and-butter pudding, Babs explained how she was seeking, even after all these years, a church with which she could feel at ease. Rose had recently converted to born-again Christianity and suggested she attend one of the meetings. Babs considered the offer — or was it a challenge? — and agreed, but only on the condition that someone else also went along.

This was why, that Sunday, I found myself sitting between the two women from the dance class, in the middle of the congregation. I had no particular religious views and hoped I had come with an open mind.

Eventually, when everyone was seated and quiet, the minister on stage said a few words of welcome. He then invited members to join him and talk of their experiences, which resulted in a long line of people telling of how they had found God and the many ways in which this had altered their lives.

There were married couples, single people, old and young, men and women; virtually every conceivable variety of humanity. It was fascinating to hear of their faith and happiness. Secretly, I envied them. Next to me, the ramrod posture and grim expression betrayed a growing tension in Babs. Coming from Leeds, she was not one to mince her words and had warned beforehand that she would 'be off' if she didn't like what took place.

Just as a young woman had finished her story and was walking off the stage, a man in front of us jumped up and cried, 'I have seen the Lord!' He was joined immediately by several others and then it seemed that everyone was out of their seats, calling and putting their hands in the air. The atmosphere was electric.

I was a little startled, but they appeared so full of joy I could not help feeling pleased for them. When everyone had sat down again, the minister said a few prayers. He then told how he was raising funds for a local charity, and explained in great depth all the good that could be achieved with the money.

The response was amazing. People throughout the hall leapt up and shouted that they would sell their cars and possessions and donate the proceeds, while others clapped and praised the Lord for all they were worth. If Babs had made her exit then, we would both have probably left unnoticed.

But it was while the hall was hushed, apart from the occasional 'Praise the Lord', and a small girl was on the stage recounting a dream from the previous night, that it all proved too much. Babs picked up her handbag and hissed, 'I'm going. You can come with me now or I'm sure someone else will take you later on.'

And with that, she was off. I looked helplessly at Rose, who, however, was watching the retreating figure with an expression of increasing horror. The school was in the country, miles from my lodging and I was thrown into turmoil at this unexpected turn of events. It was pure instinct that made me stand up and follow. Why is it, throughout my life, I so often find myself in these embarrassing situations?

The hall was silent as I squeezed my way along the row, muttering apologies at every second pair of feet. Long before I reached the end, Babs was out of the door and I felt even more alone. Now, people only had me to stare at. So they did. My face burned red and as I walked to the exit my footsteps snapped like pistol shots.

This was why, moments later, two members of the congregation had pursued me when I was outside, still trying to catch up with Babs, and attempted to persuade me to remain. I was obviously considered 'saveable', but my decision to leave had been made and we were soon careering down country lanes, hawthorn, ash and sycamore flashing by either side of the car. After a mile or so Babs said quietly,

'I'm sorry. It wasn't for me.'

We carried on. It became apparent that, in her haste, Babs had taken a wrong turn and we were, if not actually lost, certainly not heading back to Watford on the road we had taken earlier. With exaggerated exasperation, I asked,

'Babs, where are you taking me?'

She replied without turning her head.

'Don't worry. Wherever we go ... I'll be gentle with you,' and burst out laughing, as she did so often.

I lodged with Mr and Mrs Wilcox in Gammons Lane, and the following morning woke with a dull ache in the small of my back. After Babs and I had finally found our way to Watford, I had played tennis with Paul, who had a room downstairs, and assumed I had strained a muscle. I lay quietly looking at the ceiling, which was not far from my head. This had nothing to do with the rooms having low ceilings, but rather that the bed was so high.

On top of an engineering feat of metalwork was a base that supported a mattress so heavy it needed two men to lift it. One night, during the early hours, the base had slipped, leaving the mattress at a crazy angle. There was simply nothing I could do with it on my own, so I had spent the remainder of the night sleeping in a muddled heap at the lowest point.

Apart from the bed, table and chair, there was a wardrobe, chest-of-drawers and an easy chair. The linoleum was covered, though not entirely, by one of those large rugs made up of dark green and brown squares, the sort you see so often in museum houses refurbished to illustrate bygone days. There was a gas fire and, as this could be used at no extra cost, it was a cheerful companion. The house itself was spacious and clean, while the large garden at the back offered a fair amount of seclusion.

There were two other lodgers. I rarely saw the man who had a room along the corridor. Even though we shared a bathroom, I bumped into him only a handful of times. My rent included breakfast and evening meal, which Mr Wilcox brought to my room at a set time. When finished, I returned the tray to the door of their private part of the house. By the time he brought my cereal and toast that particular morning, the pain had gone and was quickly forgotten.

Watford boasted one of the best printing colleges in the country and when I had left school at eighteen I had ended up working for a printer in the North-East. After three years, it was time to move on and I was fortunate enough to obtain a place on the Higher National Diploma in Printing course, at Watford College.

The second year was out in industry and my 'filling' was to be at a large printing group in York called Ben Johnson.

However, I had a two-week break before starting and so, on Monday 6th July, I boarded a train at Kings Cross bound for Newcastle. My first year completed successfully, I felt elated and excited ... with no idea of the very different journey I would have to make, because of a long-forgotten ache in the small of my back.

Mam and Dad lived in a block of flats just off Gateshead High Street. I had been brought up there, but it had never been home, even to them, and they eventually spent thirty-five years there, until his retirement. When we were out, we never 'went home', but 'back to the flats'. It was a grim place. Desperate to get out of private service, Dad had accepted the job of caretaker, so upon the completion of the block in 1957 they were some of the first to move in, along with my elder brothers, Bob and Michael.

But Mam and Dad had grown up in the country and the decision to create an eight-lane flyover only a few paces away from the building was anathema to them. The noise and smell of traffic were forever in the air.

I had shared one of the two bedrooms with my brothers until they each got married; Michael, the middle one, leaving when I was fifteen. Apart from the bedrooms, there was a small kitchen, a bathroom and a sitting room. That was it. We had lived on top of each other in our little concrete box, without even a garden or yard to escape to.

Before leaving for York I was determined to fit as much as humanly possible into my short visit, starting the following evening with a trip to the Gateshead Pipe Band. My love for everything to do with Scotland was in my blood, as both Mam and Dad had Scottish roots. However, it was the chemistry teacher at school who had introduced me to the noble pipes, demonstrating how to play the practice chanter during lunch breaks.

We later joined the band together and I played with them for a couple of years, prior to leaving for college. When I arrived at the Bensham Community Centre, where the band practised every Tuesday, there was much shaking of hands and slapping of backs.

I had seen a fair amount of the North-East playing with the band, and it felt good to return to the hall where we had spent so many hours practising not only our playing, but also the art of marching. When the instruments had been tuned to the satisfaction of Ron Miller, the Pipe Major, we fell in line, with Ron, Ted (the chemistry teacher) and me in the front row. Behind us were John, Norman and Reg, with more behind them. Twelve in all.

We stood in silence, apart from the soft 'whooosh' of air blown gently into the bags, enough to inflate them, but not so much that it made a drone gurgle or squeak. Stand erect. Eyes ahead. *Whooosh ... whooosh.*

'By the leeeeft.'

Ron's voice boomed through the air like the fog horn on Tynemouth pier.

'Quuuuick ... march.'

The last word was spat out and joined immediately by the roar of twelve sets of bagpipes vibrating as one. The sound was deafening in the confined space. Left, right, left, right tapped our feet as we picked up the note 'E', which we always played before we launched into the first tune. Seven ... eight... nine. Almost there; Ron's trained ear listening, waiting until we all had that one note. Nine ... ten ... feet almost dancing in our shoes, as we waited for the signal to start marching.

7

We kept our eyes on Ron and when he turned his head we were off, tunes tumbling from our fingers like a waterfall in flood; 'Teribus', 'Corriechoillie', 'All the Blue Bonnets', 'The Badge of Scotland'. On and on we marched, turning when we reached a wall and walking through the ranks of those going the other way, months of practice making the movement automatic, smooth and precise.

All the while we played, and as our feet strode side by side and our fingers moved like reflections, so our thoughts became one ... and we were no longer in the community centre, no longer wearing jumpers and trousers, or living around the corner in a bungalow or a block of flats. There were no memories of faded youth or hopes long dashed.

We were up there, in the glens, hundreds of pipes and drums leading thousands of Highlanders into the valleys of history. You could feel it; more than tradition and culture. It was in the music; in the very wood of the pipes themselves. It enveloped us and we understood in our hearts why men had followed the sound into battle. I had almost forgotten the feeling, and that was unforgivable.

The next morning, the pain was worse than it had been on the previous occasion. I took two Anadins with a cup of tea, which I drank whilst leaning against the radiator in the sitting room, talking to Mam who was in the armchair next to the sickly pale yellow tiles that surrounded the electric fire on the wall.

She looked, as she often did, like Joan Hickson playing Miss Marple; her head tilted to one side, listening intently to what someone was saying. Mam was a gentle soul, who always longed to return to the countryside, away from the noise and pollution.

Through the window I could see the printing company I had left in the autumn. Was it really only ten months? It seemed that so much had happened since then. Long before I had joined, the sign on the outside of the building had lost its 'P' and, for years, the business had announced to the world that they were 'rinters'.

I could remember before it was built, when each November the local kids would build a huge bonfire on the wasteland. Our family used to watch through the window, the flat being on the first floor. It was a wise precaution considering the number of rockets and fireworks thrown about. Despite the distance, you could feel the heat from the fire on the glass.

The company had been a strange, cruel place; an adult version of the worst school playground. Bullying was rife, along with racism, sexism and every other '-ism' you might care to imagine. Even customers were not immune. One poor man from a local theatre, whose programme we printed every month, faced a barrage of shouted insults each time he came to approve the proofs of the next job.

This seemed crazy to me. He helped to pay our wages and could have taken the job elsewhere. But even with this knowledge, men on the shop floor were compelled to hurl abuse as soon as the rather flamboyantly dressed customer walked through the door. Maybe they knew, as did the man, that such a reception waited for him at every nearby printing company. They were still producing those theatre programmes when I left.

Mam and I chatted. Making a cup of tea for someone and having a good old blether were her forte. Dad was somewhere in the block and would soon be returning for his mid-morning tea. They hoped to visit me in York as Watford had been too far and we agreed that, after I had settled, we would arrange a date. As we talked, the pain gradually disappeared and by the time I heard the jingling of Dad's enormous set of keys, it was almost gone. Mam suggested toast ... and I gave it no more thought.

Chapter Two

The college had arranged for me to stay at a house in Eldon Street, not far from York's city centre, though it turned out to be quite some distance from Ben Johnson's. There were two other men and two women, and although I would have my own bedroom, I was to share bathroom, kitchen and chores. I arrived at York station with a rucksack on my back and my pipe case in one hand. The city was alive and exciting and I wound down the taxi window to soak in the atmosphere.

It was only as I rang the doorbell that it struck me I hadn't checked if anyone would be there and the foolishness of this dawned for the first time. As it happened, I was greeted by one of the largest smiles, surrounded by one of the biggest ginger beards, I had ever seen. Neil had a heart to match. He had been lodging at the house for some years, and while I deposited my belongings upstairs, Neil made coffee and produced a map of the local area so that we could work out the best route for me to take to the printing company the following morning.

Over the four large wooden desks were four stooped heads; orderliness and attention to detail stamped, metaphorically, on top of each pate. Initially, I was to spend time in the estimating department, a silent place apart from the tapping of calculator keys and the occasional telephone call.

The print estimator has a calculation for everything. For each job he'll work out how much paper to order for the number of copies, the quantity of ink required for the text and images, and the production time needed, depending upon the equipment used. In sensitive fingers, he can pick up a sheet of paper and, by feel, tell its weight; by rattling it make a good guess as to what the paper is made of; and, by its appearance, decide what jobs the stock is suitable for. Much of the work was similar to what I had carried out at the company in Gateshead, but there was still knowledge to be gleaned from these quietly spoken men.

The next morning, I arrived with my pipes in their black case and as soon as it was twelve o'clock I caught a bus outside the factory, getting off near Bridge Street, which crosses the river Ouse. I had never busked before, yet the idea appealed as a way of supplementing my grant, which was all I had to live on during my time at Ben Johnson. It had seemed a good idea, but my nerve began to fail as I stood on the bridge, tourists and locals passing by on their lunch break.

Eventually, I plucked up courage and took out the pipes, a few people stopping to watch, wondering what I was doing. A similar thought was going through my mind. However, once I started playing the reaction was better than I could have hoped for and by the end of the half hour there were about five pounds in my case. I took the pipes with me on several occasions during those first two weeks, but busking during a lunch break didn't allow much time, and while the traffic noise kept performers with quieter instruments off the bridge, the fumes were a bit unpleasant.

The following Saturday was clear and bright, so I left the house and walked down Gillygate, through Bootham Bar, passed the Minster and on to my first choice, Kings Square. A young girl playing the violin had beaten me to it. She was good and had gathered an interested crowd of shoppers. But luck was on my side. There wasn't a musician in sight at the next best option, St Sampson's Square. One of the prime busking spots was mine for the taking and I quickly claimed a place in the centre.

There were several benches nearby and a fair cross-section of people were already sitting, reading papers or resting from some early morning shopping. As I opened my case and took out the pipes, I could see several looking over curiously. I fitted the base together, put the bag under my left arm and began to blow down the mouthpiece. There was a sudden roar as the reeds burst into life, and I reached up quickly to lay my palm on the end of two of the drones. The brief blockage of air flow stopped the reeds vibrating.

Pipes are tuned by moving the sections of the drone up or down, the longer the 'tube', the lower the note. I did this with the one tenor that was still working until I was satisfied it matched the 'A' on the chanter. Putting a finger into the end of the next drone and pulling it out sharply, set the reed in this one vibrating.

As I was tuning the pipes there was a scream. In the doorway of one of the little shops that enclosed the square, stood a lady of enormous proportions, her chubby hands clamped tightly over her head, which was rocking from side to side. I couldn't imagine what had happened to the poor woman to send her into such a state, but it had nothing to do with me so I continued.

When tuning pipes, you have to listen to the 'beat' between the drones. As the frequencies of the notes become nearer, so this beat becomes faster, until finally it disappears altogether when they are in tune. As I was completing this, the scream came again. With great determination the woman hurled herself into the outer ring of people and those who didn't move quickly were pushed aside, as if they were no more than matchstick figures in a Lowry painting.

Soon she was breaking through the inner ring and, as she did so, she raised both arms high above her head and started shouting quite hysterically 'Stop! Stop!' As this quivering mass of thrashing arms and pumping legs came lumbering in my direction, I was enveloped by a great sense of impending disaster. Another of life's embarrassing moments was about to descend upon me.

'Sttoooopp!' she shouted into my face, her huge heaving breasts challenging me to defy her.

The pipes gurgled grudgingly into silence. The square was now overflowing with shoppers and tourists, all of whom had fallen into a deathly hush. Rarely had a busker in York had such a captive audience. At first, the woman was speechless after her exertion then she launched into a frightening verbal attack, her voice becoming higher in pitch and volume with every word.

'I've put up with clarinettists ... I've put up with saxo-phonists ... I've even had to listen to half orchestras, but I draw the line at ... at ... *bagpipes!*'

The last word was said with such passion that several nearby people flinched. The crowd watched the woman. She glared down at me. My gaze dropped to the pipes. With no air in the bag they were sad and droopy. I knew exactly how they felt.

Dignity, while in full retreat, is difficult, but I did my best. With as much statesmanship as possible I took apart the base drone and, with great care, put the pipes into their box. They gave one last symbolic grumble of protest before the lid was closed on top of them.

Shaking my head slowly at the great loss I walked from

the square with that strange gait one acquires when trying to get away from a barking dog, when you want to move as quickly as possible without breaking into a run. I wandered around for a bit, but in the end the only place left to play was my regular fume-filled spot on the bridge.

It was late the next morning when I finally got out of bed. The pain in the small of my back, again low down on the right-hand side, had been the worst yet, while my stomach was doing cartwheels with enormous vigour. However, by lunchtime, both problems had subsided. These events still didn't concern me and during the afternoon Neil and I had a walk in the country.

The weeks passed quickly and although the mysterious pain occurred a few more times, I enjoyed seeing the local sights and being a tourist during the evenings and weekends. Indeed, it was a delight not to be studying as I had applied myself with great determination during my first year at college.

One day, when I had been at Ben Johnson for nearly two months and had migrated through various departments to the part of the factory that housed the huge printing presses, someone came to the soundproof booth I was in to tell me there was a telephone call.

'Hello Phil, it's Ken,' said the voice.

Ken, who was seconded from Her Majesty's Stationery Office, was taking a B.Sc. at Watford College. He was ringing from the HMSO plant in Gateshead where he was spending some of his time out in industry.

'There's a job going. A vacancy has come up for a printing officer for fifty-one weeks. If you get it, you'd be on full pay.'

I had roughly twelve months to complete before returning

to college and to be able to earn a wage for that period was an opportunity not to be ignored. I wasn't sure what a printing officer did, but it sounded good enough to me. The following week I was sitting in the reception at the HMSO premises, situated on the Team Valley Trading Estate. All I knew about the plant was that it produced around half of the country's telephone directories.

A craggy Scotsman finally appeared and, after the normal niceties, led me to a room where another man was already waiting. He explained that, because of a temporary internal restructure, there was a vacancy for a limited period. The interview began and it all seemed to be going well enough until John, the Scotsman, reached behind his chair and produced a pile of items, which until then had been hidden.

'Can ye jist tell us whit aw this is?'

They were objects used in the printing industry and I started off giving lengthy explanations as to their purpose. It was when we got on to identifying typefaces that I came completely unstuck, for I had never been able to tell one from another. In desperation I regurgitated a few famous names and probably covered all the samples put in front of me, only applied them to all the wrong faces. My confidence waned and I felt the interview slipping away. The formal part over, we talked about hobbies and families until it was time for me to leave.

'We'll contact ye in a few days,' said John. 'Hae a nice journey back to York.'

I didn't have a nice journey, but there was nothing I could do about it. Neil and I had a few drinks that night to commiserate, that big smile of his beaming out all evening. It was still light when we left the pub and we took our time walking back to the lodgings. The street artists had been busy and, in the deepening shadow of the Minster, a picture of Michelangelo's 'Doni Tondo' nestled beside the wild expression of a Viking chief. Tranquillity and war side by side in chalk. The next morning I was called again from the press control room to the telephone.

'Helloo, Philip. I'd jist like to let ye know that we would like tae offer ye the job as discussed yesterday, an' hope that ye can start as soon as possible.'

Though Ben Johnson were quite happy for me to stay, they were just as pleased for me to go. It was a timely move, for by then I had been in every department and had asked every question I could think of. I contacted the college and my parents and everything was arranged for me to leave the following week. My time at York was coming to an end.

Neil prepared a farewell Sunday lunch and, during the morning, I tried my utmost to ignore the waves of nausea that kept surfacing. While great forkfuls of ham and potato disappeared into an opening somewhere in the ginger beard opposite, I cut up a single carrot into ever smaller portions. It wasn't long before I rushed to the bathroom.

I was terribly sick. For a long while afterwards I sat on the edge of the bath waiting for the shaking and nausea to subside. When I finally returned, Neil had eaten his lunch and brushed off my apologies at the wasted meal. Later on, he carried my rucksack for me to the station and I said my farewells to him and to York, boarding the train to Newcastle with a feeling of foreboding.

Apart from an attack of glandular fever during my first year at college, which had forced me to go to a local GP, I had been treated for very little since being a child. As the train pulled away, I decided that the next day I would make an appointment with my own GP in Gateshead.

Chapter Three

The man who designed doctors' waiting rooms had been busy and had fitted out the one I was now sitting in exactly like that in Watford; same decor, similar assortment of non-matching chairs, duplicate magazines with the interesting pages missing. The messages plastered on the walls also bore a striking resemblance: 'Healthy Diet For Healthy Living'; 'Inoculations: What Do You Need?' 'Diabetic? No Need ...'

However, there was one very significant difference. The waiting room in Watford had only had two or three people in it when I'd visited, but this one was crowded. It seemed that everyone had something wrong with their chest and the coughing, sneezing, choking and wheezing were like an out-of-tune orchestra, in which the players never missed their turn and, once in a while, joined together for a great crescendo.

Taking the lead part was the tuba next to me, a man of generous proportions who had overflowed on to my chair. He kept mopping his brow and it looked doubtful to me if he would last out to his appointment.

On my other side was a woman cradling a baby and who also appeared to be the mother of a small boy, currently making paper aeroplanes out of a pile of 'Diet for Health' leaflets and throwing them at a bald-headed man. What he had done to deserve such an attack I didn't know, and assumed the boy thought the lack of hair offered a greater landing area for his craft. Fortunately for both, the aeroplanes were falling well short of their mark.

The scene reminded me of when I was a young boy and every six weeks, on a Saturday morning, Dad would take me to a small room on the top floor of Shepherds, Gateshead's largest department store. We would join lots of other fathers and sons to stand and watch with awe as two ageing men in white jackets produced the severest short back and sides south of the Tyne. The two men could not be surpassed in their ability to make small boys look as similar as nature would allow. I had sometimes wondered if a father had ever taken away the wrong son.

Occasionally, a man would whisper 'Oh, his mother wants it so and so.' And five minutes later, there it would be; hairs like the bristles of a stiff brush. What a legacy to leave after a lifetime's work: thousands of unwanted haircuts.

I was brought back to the present by a shout from the bald-headed man. A paper aeroplane had finally found its mark and the small boy had wisely taken refuge behind his mother.

'Next,' shouted the receptionist.

A middle-aged woman stood up, but she had only taken a few steps when someone entered the waiting room who was obviously a friend.

'Eeee,' said the newcomer.

'Eeee,' said the first woman.

'Is it the same ...?' asked the newcomer, not finishing the sentence, but making a face instead.

The first woman continued to walk towards the corridor and the other towards the counter, so that the two moved further apart.

'Aye.'

'Oooo.'

When they were at opposite ends of the room, all heads

swung back and forth in order to follow the conversation, but by then it consisted mainly of mouthed expressions and no secrets were revealed. More people came in. When virtually the entire orchestra had been replaced with new players and even the tuba had wheezed his way off stage, the time came when 'Next' was for me.

I walked down the corridor and knocked on the relevant door. As it happened, my own GP was on holiday and so the appointment was with one of his partners whom I had not met before.

'Come in,' she said. 'What's the problem?'

I remained standing and told her about the pain low down on the right-hand side and explained about the sickness. She listened, while drying her hands on a paper towel.

'Lift up your shirt,' she said, walking towards me.

She stood in front of me and placed two slightly damp hands on each side of my back.

'Yes,' she said almost straight away. 'You have a kidney infection. I'll prescribe some antibiotics. Take them as directed and that should clear it up.'

As I tucked in my shirt she wrote out the prescription. I was genuinely impressed. The ability to tell so much by touch was a great skill indeed, although I was rather surprised she carried out no tests. As I left, I realised I hadn't even sat down.

An hour later, I was walking away from the bus stop on the Team Valley Trading Estate towards the HMSO premises. It was my fifth day at the plant and I reckoned I had the place, and the people, fairly well figured out. The building was in two parts; the small white tower block housed the offices, boardroom, canteen and social facilities (bar and snooker table), while the adjoining single-storey factory, spread out over acres of land, contained the enormous printing presses and equipment used to produce the telephone directories.

On my first morning I had been met by the Scotsman who had interviewed me. He showed me around, explaining as we passed through different departments what I would be doing during my twelve-month stay. I had become a Civil Servant and even had to sign the Official Secrets Act, although it was a mystery to me what secrets lurked in the depths of a telephone directory. As the tour came to an end, he referred to the interview.

'It was a guid job that ye got so many of those items wrong during the interview, ye knaw.'

I look at him puzzled.

'We were a bit concerned ye would be far too over-qualified for the job, but after we met ye, we could see that ye weren't very clever after aal.'

For the next six months I was to work in the costing department, which was basically a place for checking that the output figures from the presses — the man hours, paper and materials consumed — tallied with the original order. It was figures work and by the end of the first week I felt I had learnt most of what there was to know.

That Friday evening I ate supper with my parents around the small kitchen table ('dinner' was the meal we ate at noon). It was one of Dad's earlier works and had white painted legs with a yellow Formica top. The meal was fish fingers. Mam had once read that eating fish was good for the brain, and although we never quite progressed to the real thing, fish fingers were a staple part of our diet when I was growing up.

The heavy *thump thump* of pop music filtered incessantly

through the window from the working men's club over the road, to assault our ears without mercy. I hated the sound, which would go on until eleven o'clock, as it did every night apart from Sundays, when it stopped an hour earlier.

For years I had sat at the kitchen table with an old Imperial typewriter, trying desperately to commit to paper the myriad of ideas for stories and plays that whirled constantly inside my head. But creative thought or study had to battle with the noise and sheer claustrophobia of being surrounded by so much tightly fitting concrete; as though we were clothed in it. I generally lost the fight and would end up pacing the floor in frustration.

The bottle of antibiotics was on top of our small fridge and I had taken one before supper. We discussed what the doctor had said. To us, she belonged to another world and we certainly didn't know anyone who knew one socially. They were ... *different.* On the rare occasion of a visit during my childhood, a mystical figure would be shown with great reverence into the bedroom and I would lie in as much fear of this silent person as of the illness.

The doctor would delve into his magical bag, which never seemed to leave his side, and bring out strange objects that were completely incomprehensible, and which no one bothered to explain. That all adults appeared to hold this person in such awe was etched deeply into my young mind, and I recall the turmoil created by the prospect of a visit.

The GP did not even have to give you anything; the very fact that he had seen you was enough, because if he didn't leave a prescription then the illness couldn't be so bad after all. Everyone's mind was put at rest. We never considered that the condition might have been untreatable, or that he simply hadn't a clue what was wrong!

Though they might not have asked to be so, they were the demigods of society. We made them so as children. And even with the logic of adulthood, when one knew they could not possibly cure everything, there was still some untouched fragment that believed in the demigod. So my parents and I sat around the kitchen table, talked above the *thump thump*, ate our fish fingers and were relieved that the solution to my recent ill-health was so straightforward.

That Saturday there was a Scottish country dance at the Gateshead Technical College. I had been exposed to the activity because of playing in the pipe band and had been enthralled instantly. There was something about these nights that I have tried to explain to non-dancers many times, but have never come near to succeeding.

It's partly physical, the exercise and movement; partly the music and the company of friends, even dressing up for the evening. But it's much more. When you're on the floor, sounds filling your head while walls and faces blur as you twirled, spun and whirled around – there's a magic that was impossible to define. The dance made me feel I had fully returned north.

By my third week at the HMSO factory I realised that six months of 'costing' was going to be pretty fruitless from a learning point of view, so managed to arrange to spend a few hours every week in different departments on the shop floor. Apart from anything else, this provided a chance to get away from the rather oppressive atmosphere that hung around the office.

It didn't take long to work out that one of the most important focal points was the social club, and the committees that belonged to it were numerous. There were snooker, darts and table tennis leagues, as well as several sports tournaments, while those with less ambitious physical aims could join one of the many groups such as the photographic club. It made up for much, I suppose, when every day all people did was produce thousands upon thousands of telephone directories.

One morning, about three weeks after I had seen the doctor, Mam knocked on the bedroom door to let me know it was time to get ready for work. It was seven-thirty. I lay for a few moments, then leapt out of bed and ran to the bathroom. Emerging ten minutes later, white and shaky, I returned to bed and when I woke several hours later the pain was just a dull ache. Mam had already telephoned the factory and I arrived around lunchtime.

Two days later I was standing with my shirt off in front of the GP I had had before I left for college. He was somewhere in his early forties, an age where he could combine physical strength with wisdom and knowledge. He knew things we mortals would never even begin to understand.

The doctor proceeded with his examination, asking me to bend in various directions while he ran his hands up and down my back. That he was another person, with a family and hobbies, fears and weaknesses, good and bad days, did not occur to me. I didn't want to know these things; didn't want to know his first name. He might have been called something like Albert, and who'd ever heard of a demigod called Albert?

Like most people of my age I regarded good health as a right and this recent illness was an irritating inconvenience. I explained my symptoms, repeating what I had said to his partner. He dismissed her diagnosis with a wave of his hand and a rather scornful expression towards a wall.

'Well, you need to sleep on something a bit firmer, so I

suggest you put a board under your mattress. Be wary of your posture and the types of chairs you sit in and be careful how you lift anything that might be heavy.'

If I was puzzled by this diagnosis then I did my best to conceal it. However, this treatment was as different as could be. The idea of questioning him was unthinkable, so I thanked him for his time and left. Later on, Dad and I moved some of the bedroom furniture, making room to lay my mattress on the floor. At the weekend, we invested in a large piece of rigid board, which we placed under the mattress having put the bed back together. It didn't make any difference and towards the end of November I was at the surgery again. This time the GP arranged for me to have an X-ray at the local hospital.

'Follow the yellow line,' said the girl behind the hospital reception desk, pointing to the floor at a mass of coloured lines, which disappeared in various directions. 'You'll find the X-ray department at the end.'

I stuck closely to my guide, down corridors and through doors, passing others following their own colours, red to physiotherapy, blue to pathology, green to pharmacy. We were like variations of Inspector Clouseau pursuing a vital clue to a murder. Perhaps we would all arrive at the same spot, where there would be a body with a knife stuck in the chest. Eventually, my line stopped at the bottom of a pair of large doors marked 'X Ray Dept'.

There didn't seem to be a reception, but someone directed me around the corner where a nurse produced a list with my name on and asked me to accompany her to the changing rooms. On the way we passed a middle-aged chap in a white smock. He must have had a peculiar complaint because he walked with a strange crab-like movement, his back against one wall. I hoped they could soon find a cure for him.

The changing rooms turned out to be a row of small cubicles. I entered one and pulled the curtain closed behind me, as instructed. Apart from two pegs on the wall and a chair, the only other item was something that looked like a folded sheet. I undressed, placing my clothes in a neat pile on the chair, and picked up the gown.

The thing was enormous. First of all I tried putting it on like a bath robe, but having the opening at the front resulted in the most indecent exposure of my credentials, so I took it off and slipped my arms through, putting the opening behind me. However, the garment was designed so that no matter how hard one tried, the cords couldn't be tied tight enough to come anywhere near closing the opening.

I was still working out ways to overcome this when a voice called from the other side of the curtain. I stuck my head out and a nurse who looked about fifteen asked me to go with her. Hesitantly, I left the safety of the cubicle and followed her along the corridor with a crab-like walk, my back against one wall.

She led me into a room where I was handed into the care of the radiographer, who checked my name and address then asked me to stand behind a square metal plate. While I did this, she disappeared behind a large screen, her face appearing at a small glass window moments later.

'Mr Paris, when I say, I want you to hold your breath.' The words echoed off the hard surfaces in the room, making her voice sound harsh and tinny. 'I'll tell you when to let it out.'

'Right,' I shouted back, hoping she wouldn't forget.

'There's one more thing I want you to do.'

'What's that?' I asked.

'Smile,' she said.

Chapter Four

It was mid-afternoon, about a week before Christmas. The aching had started shortly after nine and grown more intense as the morning passed. Gnawing. Gnawing. The silence of the office only served to intensify it, so that in the end I could think of nothing else. During the lunch break I took two of the painkillers that the doctor had prescribed when I had gone to get the results of the X-rays. These had not revealed anything abnormal and he had advised me to allow more time.

Now the tablets had done their job and the pain was replaced with the most overwhelming tiredness I had ever known. It wasn't just weariness it was an all-consuming exhaustion. I had been staring at the papers spread out on my desk for the last thirty minutes without doing any work. They were the production sheets for Nottingham's alpha telephone directory; a job that had been completed in the finishing department a few days earlier and was already being despatched to various post offices around the city.

There were sheets from the platemaking and composing rooms, returns from the bindery and the transport office, T30 forms, T10 forms, distribution lists for head office. The figures whirled in front of my eyes like a hundred caterpillars doing the eightsome reel. Round and round they went, little hairy lines spinning and turning; obscene figures, mocking and laughing as they danced because I couldn't catch them.

One of the managers worked at a desk just along from

mine and I sat with my head resting in my left hand, holding a pencil in my right, with which I scribbled on a large pad. I had sensed early on that ill-health would not go down well in the office, and was determined to hide it as much as possible. To maintain the illusion of activity, I tapped loudly on the big desk calculator.

Invisible threads were pulling down my eyelids. I felt drugged and started to have the most tormenting fantasies about sleep. *Sleeeep.* My comfortable, familiar bed was floating on a gently rocking sea, head cradled in the softest of pillows, the sun caressing my body, warming me to the very marrow of my bones. *Drifting.* I would have given so much just to sleep for a few minutes.

I had to close my eyes. I reckoned I could risk perhaps ten seconds at a time without anyone noticing; a few moments of bliss to take away the stinging. I started to count the seconds and when I got to six my head slipped in my hand and I shot up with a start.

The manager looked over so I tapped vigorously on the calculator, examining the figures on the display panel with an expression of great concentration and making 'Mmmm' noises. He went back to his work. I decided to get out of the office so went to the gents.

Locking myself in a cubicle I collapsed against the door. In here I could at least close my eyes for a few moments without fear of anyone seeing me. I would allow myself two minutes and then go back. Before the first was up, my body was sliding down the door. This was madness. Leaving the cubicle, I walked over to one of the sinks and splashed cold water on my face.

It felt as if I had fallen into a deep well of cotton wool. There were no walls, nothing to hang on to and no way of

28

climbing out. Instead, all around me was delicate softness; comforting, hypnotising, promising to rid me of all my troubles if I only gave in. I couldn't fight it. Warm inviting fingers wrapped themselves around my arms and legs, pulling me gently back into the cocoon. *Sleeeep,* whispered the cotton wool voice.

I slapped my face. The sharp stinging was like a ladder being thrown down into the well and I grabbed the nearest rung, although it still felt as though part of my brain wasn't working. I repeated the treatment. My drastic action began to have some effect and, after about fifteen minutes, I returned to the office and the hairy dancing figures.

Fortunately, a flexi-time system operated at the factory, which meant I could leave at four-thirty. The work wasn't a problem, for I could finish quickly in the morning anything not completed that afternoon. It was just a matter of sitting it out and keeping up the pretence.

At thirty-five minutes past four I was waiting for the bus that always came through the trading estate at that time to pick up workers who finished on the half hour. The vehicle was soon almost full with people from the biscuit and linen factories, those from the other large printing companies, De La Rue and Waddingtons. I dared not close my eyes for fear of ending up miles beyond my stop.

The sight of my bed was a cause of unbelievable elation. My mattress, moulded to my shape, the sheets and soft pillows beckoning me. An old friend. As I pulled the blankets up to my chin, I saw Dad standing at the door with a hot water bottle, which he was wrapping in a towel so it wouldn't burn my skin. But before he had even walked across the room, I was fast asleep.

* * *

'Poor devil! See him owre his trash,
As feckless as a wither'd rash,
His spindle shank a guid whip-lash,
His nieve a nit:
Thro' bloody flood or field to dash,
O how unfit!'

It was one of those things you don't want to do, but you agree anyway in order to help someone in a fix. The local rugby club was holding a Burns night.

'We've tried the normal pipers, but the good ones are already booked,' the man had said over the telephone only a few weeks earlier. Now, as I looked down at the large silver platter upon which lay an enormous haggis, its skin the colour and texture of grey sandstone, I was beginning to realise why I had had reservations.

'But that's raw,' I said with something near revulsion, pointing at the offending item that had just been laid on the floor nearby.

'Yes, yes. That's alright,' said my companion (someone big in the rugby club who was going to carry out the 'address'). 'The cooked stuff is in the kitchen ready to serve after we've gone through the ceremony.'

As I looked at him my heart was sinking steadily. He continued his rehearsal.

'... But mar the Rustic, haggis-fed
The trembling earth resounds his tread! ...'

We were alone in the corridor that led into the main hall, where the club members, wives and guests had been gathering for the last twenty minutes. I peered around the door; the third time I had done so since arriving more than half an hour earlier.

The top table, where the action was going to take place,

was at the far end of the hall. The idea was that we would take the longest route, passing close to as many people as possible. When it was all over, we would take the shortest path back. As soon as we were out of sight the kitchen staff would rush in and begin serving the first course. It seemed simple enough.

'... The groaning trencher there ye fill ...'

The man was pacing up and down, stopping occasionally at a particular passage in the poem to bend over the platter then he would shout and rave at the lump of dead meat with the greatest of passion. Strangely, it seemed completely un-moved by this.

I checked myself over for the last time. Brogues neatly polished, cable-patterned white hose (knitted by Mam), *sgian dubh* tucked into the right one, kilt, sporran hanging straight, belt with buckle buffed and shining, white shirt, black jacket, tartan tie, and a Glengarry on my head. Even the pipes had been given a rub with a duster. I now picked these up and started blowing gently down the mouthpiece in order to have something to do.

Someone stuck their head around the door and told us we were on in less than five minutes. My companion smiled nervously and put away his notes. We lined up: me with pipes on shoulder; him standing behind with platter held at chest height. The sheepskin bag was almost full and when we got the signal I squeezed hard with my elbow and the pipes roared into life. I started into the slow air 'My Home', tapping my feet in time. Behind me, haggis and man stood to attention.

The noise echoed in the confines of the corridor, but I knew that the music would be filtering through into the hall and would infect the audience with great anticipation and excitement … or, more likely, dread. Years of piping had taught me that the best way to walk through a doorway is not to bend your legs, a rather ungainly posture, but to lift up the bag so that the drones drop horizontally across the shoulder. In this grand manner, I entered and hoped that the haggis was keeping up.

Slowly, and with great aplomb, we made our way through the aisles, every turn taking us nearer to our destination. People stood and followed our progress, clapping to the tune. I was into my second slow march when we finally arrived at the top table and I took my position just to one side behind it, leaving enough room for the haggis bearer to pass and lay down his burden.

The secret to a sharp finish is to stop blowing several bars before you want the music to end and then when you get there to lift your arm away quickly from the bag so the air flow stops instantly. People sat down and the hall fell into a deathly silence.

'Fair fa' your honest sonsie face,
Great chieftain o' the puddin'–race!
Aboon them a' ye tak your place,
Painch, tripe, or thairm:
Weel are ye wordy o' a grace
As lang's my arm ...'

It was a noble start and only the haggis continued to look unimpressed, as the man from the rugby club waved around his arms as if fighting off a horde of wasps. I think nature has been particularly unkind to me in several ways, not least in that when I am placed in situations demanding great dignity and decorum I am inevitably struck down by an uncontrollable urge to laugh. I looked at everything except the billowing arms.

On the table, apart from the haggis, there was a *sgian dubh* and two small tumblers half-full of a clear golden liquid, which was to be downed in one at the end of the ceremony. Now, at that age, one measure of whisky would probably have lasted me an entire week, so I had arranged earlier with the barman for my glass to contain cider, and trusted that no one would be interested enough to notice.

His face glowing quite red with heat, exertion and emotion, the man carrying out the address lifted up the *sgian dubh*. With a huge flourish of showmanship, he pulled it from the sheath and held the blade high in the air. The corners of my mouth started to twitch and I scratched my nose to hide it.

'His knife see rustic Labour dight,

An' cut you up wi' ready sleight …'

He sunk the blade into the haggis as if plunging a stake into Count Dracula. *If it wasn't dead before, then it certainly is now,* I thought.

'Trenching your gushing entrails bright

Like ony ditch:

And then, O what a glorious sight

Warm-reekin', rich!'

What is actually supposed to happen at this point is that when the skin is slit, the cooked haggis gushes over the plate releasing clouds of steam and juicy smells into the air. It's quite dramatic when done properly. The raw food refused to gush, look like a glorious sight or indeed do anything, except lie there like several pounds of uncooked meat; the hilt pointing skywards like a miniature version of the sword in the stone.

'… Then, horn for horn they stretch an' strive …'

This was surely an award-winning performance and the

audience were riveted. Grasping the handle he pulled, but instead of the blade coming out, the entire haggis lifted off the platter. He put it down and tried again, but the knife was well-embedded. I was permanently scratching my nose. Grabbing hold of the haggis in one hand and the *sgian dubh* in the other, he heaved, his voice getting even higher and louder as he continued with great gusto.

'Is there that o'er his French ragout ...'

Suddenly, the *sgian dubh* shot out and the haggis rolled across the table. The man proved his sporting abilities, and a save that would have been commendable on the famous playing fields of Bradford stopped the haggis from disappearing over the edge.

To my shame, it was all too much. I started to laugh and although I did my best to hide it, the pipes bouncing around on my shoulder were a giveaway. On and on he went, getting redder in the face, until finally he reached the last line of Burns' poem in a great crescendo of emotion and vigour.

'But, if ye wish her gratefu' prayer,

Gie her a Haggis!'

The audience were spellbound and his Oscar guaranteed. But the performance was not over yet. He picked up his tumbler, raised it in the air and turned to me. I had once more become a part of everyone's attention so, attempting to match the drama of the moment, picked up the other glass and raised that for all to see.

We emptied the contents in one and banged our tumblers loudly on the table, for extra effect. As I let go of the glass, the world about me blurred, as if somehow I was no longer a part of it, only an onlooker standing the wrong side of a frosted window. It was the roughest badger's-arse whisky I had ever tasted. My throat on fire, I gasped like a drowning man coming up for air and doubled over in an uncontrollable fit of coughing.

I was utterly helpless. The pipes fell off my shoulder while tears fell freely upon my brogues and 200 people watched, some no doubt wondering if this was part of the normal proceedings. However, even in this state, some part of my mind registered that my only salvation lay in getting out of the hall. With an enormous effort, I started blowing, and coughing, down the mouthpiece.

As soon as the bag had sufficient air I squeezed it violently, the drones bursting into life. With the tears falling down my cheeks, now joined by a disgustingly running nose, I shot off blindly in what I hoped was the direction of the exit, leaving the man from the rugby club to hurry after me with the platter and wounded haggis. 'Scotland the Brave' was never meant to sound the way I played it that evening.

Everyone stood up for our departure, but several were forced to dive into their bread rolls at the terrifying vision of a snot-laden, stumbling piper heading towards them. As I neared the last table I could see that the door we had entered earlier was closed, so I blinked away enough tears to fix my eyes on the man nearest to the exit. I twitched, winked, nodded and pointed with my eyebrows so forcefully they must have looked like two cavorting caterpillars.

I was thinking I might get more reaction from the haggis when the guest realised suddenly what was needed and shot off to open the door. I almost fell through it and for the next ten minutes couldn't speak a single word. By the time I returned, everyone was tucking into their cock-a-leekie soup, my performance already relegated into history.

A place at the top table had been allocated to me and I sat down in the one empty seat. I knew no one, but this point was becoming surprisingly unimportant as a glowing feeling of friendship towards my fellow man enveloped me. Perhaps the evening was not so bad after all. A five-pound note, my fee, was now tucked safely in my sporran, and I was about to get a good meal.

'Well played, young man. Though, I thought you were a goner for a while.'

I looked along the table to the speaker, who was sitting at the far end. It was the man who had carried out the 'address'. Everybody turned to me for my reply and I did actually open my mouth to answer. However, all I could think of was the sight of him grabbing the haggis as if it was a rugby ball. Instead of thanking him or making a witty comment suitable for the occasion ... I started to laugh.

The man appeared quite taken aback for a moment and the faces around the table took on the sort of expression that appears automatically when someone in hearing vicinity commits a *faux pas* of embarrassingly large proportions. Quite unexpectedly, the man started laughing as well, and within moments everyone was rolling around and saying how funny it was, and I hadn't spoken a word. What a great night.

In the armchair across the room Mam's face was almost as ashen as mine, her hands clasping and unclasping in her lap. I was lying on the settee, my breath coming in gasps as waves of pain swept up from the small of my back and around my side. I felt dizzy with it. It was shortly after nine in the morning and I had been like this for more than two hours, the humour of the previous evening's Burns' night impossible to recall. I hadn't been able to keep down any painkillers.

'You must go to the doctor. If it's an emergency, he'll see you without an appointment.'

I nodded, but said nothing.

'I could ring for a taxi.'

'No,' I said. 'It's only a walk away.'

This was in no way meant to be an act of bravery, but we *never* rang for a taxi. Even when I was nine and split my chin, I had stood with Dad at the bus stop, holding a blood-soaked towel waiting to go to the Queen Elizabeth hospital.

After another half an hour I decided to make the journey and set off for the surgery. The waiting room was almost full. However, the receptionist told me to sit down, pointing out a man whose turn would be the one before mine. In those days doctors didn't come to fetch you and patients were given a slot on arrival. The receptionist shouted 'Next' and you had to remember your slot, sometimes arguing the point with someone who was trying to push in.

Fortunately, there were a couple of empty chairs and I collapsed into one of them. The morning wore on. Figures moved in and out of my vision as people came and left. I concentrated on the man whose turn was before mine. When he stood up, I was next. Move. Move. I felt terribly sick again, but didn't want to leave the room even for a short while in case I lost my place.

'The pain is much worse, and I'm so sick I'm losing weight,' I gasped as I fell into the seat opposite the doctor.

'You need to see a specialist,' he replied, reaching for the telephone. Moments later he was talking to someone on the other end. When the conversation was over he dialled again, speaking to me while waiting to be put through.

'I'm going to sign you off work until the specialist has seen you at your home.'

Then he was talking to someone again. He explained the problem, listened for a short while, read out my name and address and finished the call. He seemed satisfied.

'Right. The specialist will come to see you on Monday morning around eleven, and we'll take it from there. Here's a sick note,' he said writing, 'and I'm going to prescribe some stronger painkillers.'

He handed me both pieces of paper. I wasn't sure what sort of specialist was coming to see me, but felt that things were moving forward. Reinforcements were being brought in. There was nothing more I could do except hope Monday came around faster than it normally did. I thanked the doctor and headed for the chemist.

Back in the kitchen, I took two of the small white pills, went to bed and didn't wake up until late in the afternoon.

Chapter Five

In preparation for his visit (we assumed the specialist would be a 'he') the flat had been cleaned and polished, dusted and hoovered from top to bottom, side to side and back up again. No corner had been left untouched and no chair unmoved, regardless of how remote the chances were of him moving the furniture about to look underneath. Not a speck of dust or the meekest of germs dared enter the flat that Monday morning without certain and instant annihilation.

In the bathroom, where the glare from shining surfaces was almost painful to the eye, the best guest towel had been hung on the hook behind the door, and Dad and I were under strict instructions not to use it. There was a new bar of Palmolive and a fresh toilet roll on the holder, even though the other one wasn't quite finished.

In the kitchen a tray had been laid out with a cup and saucer from our china tea set. Unless you looked closely, it wasn't too noticeable that the red and gold pattern didn't meet up properly part way around. There was fresh milk in the little blue jug and a plate of Bourbon biscuits, arranged so precisely they were like tiny soldiers on parade.

I was watching out of the kitchen window while leaning against the white 'butler's' sink, the sort that today people think are trendy. We never thought it was trendy, just large and cracked, a bit like some of the neighbours. Behind me, Mam was boiling the kettle, the third time she had done so in the last twenty minutes. She wanted to be able to offer tea the moment that the specialist arrived. Mam and Dad were frantic such an important person should be visiting. She rejoined me at the window and we continued our vigil.

Across the road the fishmonger had stopped his horse and wagon outside the toilets next to the working men's club. He came around once a week and a lot of people from the flats would go out and buy their fish from him. We never did. Mam once announced, 'I bet he uses those disgusting toilets and never washes his hands.' How she knew this detailed information I didn't know, and I suspected this was more a presumption on her part than any actual knowledge.

In fairness, the fish, which were simply laid out on the open wagon, always looked somehow more ... dead ... than those in the Co-op's refrigerated cabinet. On the rare occasions that I walked past nearby, there was generally a particularly unsavoury smell from the wagon. Then again, it could have been the horse or, for that matter, the fishmonger. Having said all this, he didn't actually sell fish fingers so was on a bit of a loser from the start.

When the car pulled up we called Dad from the sitting room and rushed to the front door, which we opened and stood in a line along the corridor; Dad, Mam, then me further along, halfway to the bedroom. As he entered our tiny flat we were almost washed away by his confidence, which flowed before him like a river, brushing us aside as if we were no more than dried autumn leaves that had landed too close to the bank.

All offers of tea and Bourbon biscuits were refused with a shake of the head that was little more than a tic. And so only a few moments after his arrival, I stood, arms pointing to the bedroom ceiling, naked apart from a pair of Marks & Spencer's underpants that Mam had purchased on Saturday especially for the occasion.

'Stretch out your arms in front of you,' said the specialist. He had walked behind me. I did as told and once again he ran his hands down my back and then along my arms.

'And move them sideways.'

He didn't have a lot to say, other than to ask me to stretch my arms, bend this way or that. I explained my symptoms during these silences, but got the impression the message wasn't getting through, so I told him it again a bit louder. I even pointed to the area of the pain, which was not in my spine at all. Indeed, I had no pain or stiffness there and swung my arms, bent this way and that way without any problem whatsoever.

'Does this hurt?' he asked, pressing against a part of my spine. No, it didn't hurt. 'Can you feel this?' Well, yes, you've got your hand there. I had to lie on the bed and go through another set of movements, while he ran his hands up and down my spine, stopping now and then at a particular disc. Then there was nothing. With my head turned away from him I could only guess he was simply standing, looking down. Eventually, he broke the silence.

'You have an inflammation of the spine.'

It was an unshakable statement. As sure as I was lying there, the fact was I had an inflammation of the spine. There was no room for doubt, debate or deviation. I heard him walk over to his case, which was on the top of the blanket-box, so I sat up on the bed. Now it was my turn to look at his back.

'I'm going to book you into hospital for a course of traction; probably about two weeks,' he said, searching the contents of his bag.

I opened my mouth, but shut it again without speaking. How could I progress from this position? If he was so certain

I had an inflammation of the spine, then I was equally certain I did not, if, for no other reason, than that I could fling myself around the dance floor for hours on end without the slightest adverse effect. Perhaps it wasn't a very medical reason, but it was my body and I was sure he was wrong.

However, I realised there was little option other than to do what he said. If I didn't, where could I go from there? It would be difficult to return to my own GP if I refused the specialist's treatment. Medical doors may well start to close and I was convinced the cause and cure had not yet been found.

It felt a bit like throwing dice in a game in the hope that, eventually, there would be a double six. The dilemma was that if you didn't play the game, you couldn't go on, so there would be no chance of winning and little hope of a cure.

It wasn't that anyone took anything less seriously or that they were less caring then they should, but what must never be forgotten is that the game belonged to the medical profession. The patient must sit across the table from the illness with the doctor between; sometimes their moves would help you win and sometimes their moves would hinder you.

Either way, it was their board and dice. Play by their rule book, or don't play at all. Throw the dice; double six to win. Mine had just rolled under the wardrobe.

Chapter Six

Day One. Monday, 1st February, 1982.

I stood at the entrance to the ward, unwilling to cross the barrier that took me from being an outsider to a patient. I hadn't stayed in hospital since my tonsils had been removed at the age of eight, but the smells and sounds of the previous ten minutes brought my childhood ordeal flooding back as if it had happened only a few days earlier.

There were seven beds each side and most had someone in residence. As I looked at the occupants, I felt even less inclined to enter. Not one of them appeared to be under sixty. At the bottom of every bed was a pulley system. A strap, which disappeared under the blankets and I assumed was attached to the patient, went over a small wheel and down to a weight that hung freely about a foot off the floor.

Some of the men also had a form of head restraint, and they looked particularly miserable. I was in the process of persuading myself there had been a mistake and this was surely the wrong ward, when a nurse appeared.

'Hello, you must be Philip.'

It crossed my mind to deny it, but before I could speak she continued.

'We were expecting you sometime this morning. Would you follow me.'

Well, it wasn't really a question, so we walked past the first three beds and stopped at the fourth, which was empty.

'If you would like to get changed, sister will be along shortly.'

Then I was left alone, standing awkwardly by the little wooden locker upon which stood the standard hospital-issue water jug and glass. Most of the patients seemed to be asleep and I stole a glance at the man in bed number five. His large tattooed arms lay on top of the blankets and I thought he looked like a sailor in one of those old black and white films about the Second World War (as it turned out later that's exactly what he had been).

Hesitantly, I began to unpack my small suitcase, the one that hardly ever got taken down from the top of the wardrobe. You have to cross a bridge when you enter hospital to stay. As I put into the locker my toothbrush, toiletries, spare pyjamas and books, I was crossing that bridge, and when I got changed I was at the other side.

You knew when you'd got there, because suddenly it was *your* bed and locker and you were ready to fight off the devil himself should he try to remove *your* chair. I was just putting away the last of my few possessions, wondering if they served fish fingers at meal times, when a voice said:

'Have you heard the one about the camel and the officer?'

I turned around. My tattooed neighbour wasn't asleep after all.

'Well ... no. I don't think so,' I answered.

'You see, this officer joins his troops in the desert and after about three weeks he's getting a bit frustrated, so he says to one of the men:

"I say, my man. What do you chaps do around here for women?"

"Well sir," says the private. "Once a month, we all go over to the compound and service the camels."

"Oh, I say, that's quite frightfully disgusting," said the officer and walked away.'

I sat down on the bed as this was obviously going to be a long shaggy camel story. The officer impersonation was funny. He carried on.

'Anyway, come another five weeks, the officer can't stand it. So, this particular night, he joins the group of privates who had gathered, ready to go to the compound. All of a sudden, there's a shout and the men start running as fast as they can. So, he sets off after them and eventually manages to catch up.

"I say. I say. Why are we all running? We're only going to the camels after all," says the officer.

"Yes, sir," says a private, still running, "I know sir. But you don't want to get an ugly one."'

Even before I responded, a movement caught my eye, for up and down the ward the weights hanging over the beds were bouncing up and down as the patients attached to them rocked with laughter. I hadn't realised the other men had been listening to the joke and, despite my previous unhappy disposition, I started laughing as well.

'I'm Joe,' said my tattooed companion, stretching out a large hand.

'I'm Philip,' I replied. I put my hand somewhere in the middle of his and shook it warmly, because for all Joe's rough appearance, I recognised his joke as a kind attempt to make a nervous-looking young man more at ease.

'This is Philip, everyone,' shouted Joe.

There was a chorus of 'Hello Philip' and I nodded my head in various directions, until I felt everybody had received their fair share.

'Watch out, here comes sister,' said Joe, just loud enough for the approaching figure to hear.

'What's all this noise about? I can hear you all the way

down in the office,' she said, but with good humour.

'I wouldn't put him on traction. He's long enough as it is,' said Joe.

'Don't be giving him any of your bad habits. I'm sorry we've had to put you next to him, Philip, but it's the last bed we've got,' she said, indicating that we should sit.

'Are you going to sit on my bed next?' shouted a voice from further along the ward.

'Hey, I'm next, amn't I?' said another voice, this one with a Scottish accent.

The sister waved her hand and the men became silent. They had had their fun for the moment and knew she had a job to do. She had a clipboard and proceeded to work through a list of questions, writing down my answers on a large blue form.

We had not long completed this, and she was explaining the layout of the ward and how I would be seeing a physiotherapist the next morning, when the nurse who had shown me to the bed appeared, carrying several cloth straps, plus a circular metal disc covered in canvas. I stood up while the two pulled the bedclothes off and then I lay on the mattress, as instructed.

They unravelled the bundle and between them fixed a waistband around me. This had four straps running down to the bottom of the bed where they were attached to the main pulley system. The waistband was held by Velcro strips and I was shown how simple it was to take this off, so I could get up easily to have meals and go to the washroom; beyond that, I was to stay in bed.

The disc was attached to the end of the lead running down from the pulley wheel, and its size depended on each patient. When this was secured, the sister and nurse put the bedclothes back, made sure I was as comfortable as possible, and were gone.

The lightness of the weight surprised me for I couldn't feel it pulling at all and there was certainly no sensation of being stretched, as I had imagined previously. From my new horizontal position, I surveyed my surroundings as best I could. The chap in the bed on my right was asleep and I couldn't see much of him, but I felt that my initial impression about the general age of the occupants had been perhaps a little unfair.

Through the open door at one end of the ward I could see into a room in which there was a television mounted on one wall. Apart from the entrance, the only other door was the one that led into the washroom. The ward itself was fairly bare of furniture apart from three tables in the centre. There was a bookcase near the television room and a large clock on one wall. I continued my examination.

At first, I thought the bed on the other side of Joe's was empty, but now I could see that there was someone in it. However, the man made so little impression that it didn't appear there was anyone at all. Joe, who had the knack of appearing to be asleep when he wasn't, saw me looking over.

'That's Alfred,' he said in a whisper, turning his head towards me. 'Cancer of the spine.'

He made a face and shook his head to indicate Alfred wouldn't be walking out of the ward.

'But what are you in here for? You're a bit young to be in this place.'

'Well, to be honest, I don't think I should be here, but the specialist seems to think I have inflammation of the spine.'

'Oh. He's a good man.'

We chatted on and I began to feel more at ease. Joe told me about the hospital food. Whether this was because he thought I needed a good feed, I didn't know. Apparently, it wasn't too bad. The staff were decent with very rare exceptions, which he warned me of, and when the night shift came on at eight o'clock, everyone was allowed to get up for a few hours to watch television or play cards. Visiting was six-thirty to seven-thirty and they weren't too strict about numbers, as long as they were kept within reason.

Joe nodded off and was soon snoring loudly. I shut my eyes, but the adrenalin that had been rushing through my veins all morning had not slowed down, and a few minutes later I opened them again. From my locker I picked up a copy of *The Old Curiosity Shop*, one of those books I had always intended to read, but had never got around to. After ten minutes, my arms were aching.

It was nearly eleven o'clock. I had been there an hour and was already starting to get fidgety. My attention was taken by a young chap in a white coat, who appeared at the entrance pushing a trolley upon which were several big metal teapots and jugs, and a pile of pale blue cups and saucers.

'Tea up,' he shouted.

The effect of this announcement was quite dramatic and resulted in almost everyone sitting up in their beds, those with head restraints removing them first, of course. The young man quickly reunited cups and saucers and, in what seemed to be one continuous movement, poured tea from a pot. When he had filled about seven cups, he added varying quantities of milk and sugar and started to take them to the patients, beginning with those nearest the entrance.

He seemed to find something to say to everyone and left

each man laughing when he returned to the trolley. In this way, the tea gradually made its way closer. I pulled myself up in bed and found that I could sit up quite easily, while still attached to the weight.

'What's your poison?' asked the youth approaching.

'White, one sugar, thanks,' I replied.

What was left of the morning passed pleasantly enough. When lunch arrived all the men except three got up and, taking our chairs, we sat around the three large tables. This was my first opportunity to speak to the others and they were all interested to know *my* story. I felt like a fraud, for many of them were obviously in some discomfort.

They were a good bunch. Most were Geordies, though there were a couple of Scots and a chap from south of Darlington who had met a girl from the North-East during the war, and had settled there afterwards. They were on the ward for a variety of reasons; some had had accidents years ago, the effects of which were only now beginning to show themselves, while others had diseases of the bones. A few were perhaps just getting old.

We dragged lunch out as long as possible, but in the end we had to return to our beds and the traction. Now that I had discovered I could sit up, I was able to read without having to hold the book above my head, so the afternoon passed following the adventures of Little Nell and her grandfather, making their escape from the evil Quilp. I was brought back to the present by the arrival of a figure by my bed.

'Hello,' said the vicar cheerfully.

'Hello,' I replied, putting down my book.

'How are you feeling today?'

'Quite well, thank you.'

'Splendid. Splendid. And what are you in here for?'

'I'm told I have something wrong with my spine.'

'I see, I see. And the traction is the treatment?'

'Yes,' I replied.

The conversation went on ... and on. We covered my health, work, family, where I lived and touched on religion. Between each topic there was a pause. Joe was snoring, his face half-covered by a copy of *The Sun*, which he had been reading a little earlier. In fact, as I looked around, everyone was asleep.

Eventually, when we had discussed all the subjects we could think of, and it was obvious there was no one else to speak to, he wished me a speedy recovery and, appearing rather disappointed, left. Almost immediately Joe woke up and started to read his paper again.

'You've just missed the vicar,' I said.

'Oh no,' he replied, turning to the sports page.

Mam and Dad visited that evening. They brought the mandatory supplies of fruit and soft drink, which were deposited on the locker. There wasn't really a lot to say. I had left the flats only that morning and the visit was filled with long silences during which Mam kept saying, 'Well, it all looks very nice, dear,' while glancing rather uncertainly at the nearby mermaid tattoos.

Joe was true to his word and when the night staff came on duty we were allowed out of bed. The atmosphere changed considerably. A hard core of card players soon began a game, and very quickly the immediate area was shrouded in a pall of cigarette smoke.

It was like watching a western, where toughened cowboys tested each other's nerves with higher and higher bets, only instead of leather boots, spurs and jeans there were a variety of slippers, dressing gowns and paisley patterned pyjamas.

I hung around watching for a while then went into the television room, where those requiring slightly less physical activities had gathered to watch a documentary about the life of the albatross. We sat glued to the set as if it had been our life's passion to learn such information.

Later on, when the albatross had flown into the sunset and been replaced by the nine o'clock news, I wandered into the ward. Somewhere in the smoke the card game was still in progress. Joe was cleaning up, with nearly half the matchsticks on the table in a neat pile next to him.

'Pull up a chair,' he said.

The four men shuffled around to make room for me. I sat down, feeling rather awkward and not really belonging. Fortunately, I was soon rescued by the appearance of the tea trolley, which was left in the middle of the floor for people to help themselves.

Not everyone had got out of bed when the night staff came on duty and, apart from Alfred there were two others who were still strapped to their pulleys. Joe and a wizened old Geordie who didn't appear to have any teeth were the first to the trolley and they immediately started pouring out tea for the line that formed.

However, the mugs given to the men at the front weren't drunk by them, but instead taken to those still in bed. And there was no question of not putting one on Alfred's locker, even though a full mug was removed, and no doubt this one would also be taken away untouched later.

I had never been near to anyone who was dying and during the day had cast secret glances at the emaciated figure. Such caution had been unnecessary since Alfred was either asleep or somewhere near to it, drifting on a river of morphine, his glazed eyes staring sightlessly at the ceiling.

I wondered of how much he was conscious: if he heard the men playing cards and joking with the nurses; if he was aware of the pale and fragile woman who sat holding his hand throughout visiting hour. He must surely have known, somewhere in his subconscious, that every minute the river took him nearer to his final destination. Did he want it to run fast and clear, or was he hanging on to every passing branch to slow down his progress?

'Here you are.'

I had reached the front of the queue and Joe was holding out a large mug. When everyone had been served, we gathered around one of the patients who had remained in his bed.

'Did you enjoy your chat with the vicar then, Philip?' asked Joe in a loud voice.

'Err ... yes, thanks.'

Everyone was smiling, but I couldn't see why this should be funny and my bewildered expression made the others chuckle. Joe started to tell some more camel jokes, but it was the real-life stories that had men roaring with laughter, until someone would say, 'Shhh. Remember Alfred.'

It appeared most of them had been in the army or navy during the war, and by the second round of tea the two camps were competing fiercely to recount the funniest event. The air was so thick with stories you sucked them in with every breath until they filled you with wonder. To me, in my early twenties, it was a window to another world.

When the last remaining teapot was almost empty, and even the night staff thought enough was enough, we drifted off to clean teeth and wash. I got into bed and fixed the waistband around me just before the main light went out. I had survived my first day and that was surely going to be the hardest. Now it was only a case of sitting, or lying, it out for the next two weeks.

I could hear Joe settling himself down. After a few moments, and rather self-consciously, I whispered:

'Good night, Joe.'

'Good night,' came his gruff voice in the semi-dark.

'GOOD NIGHT, JOE,' shouted a Scot's voice from the other end of the ward.

The ward gradually fell quieter, though not silent, for there was always the noise of snoring or coughing and the occasional figure wandering to the washroom. At the far end of the ward, near the entrance and where most of the light filtered in from the corridor, a nurse sat in a chair, legs tucked underneath her and wrapped in a blanket. She would be watching over us until morning.

I shut my eyes and tried to sleep, but my mind was in a whirl with the events that had taken place during the day. Late into the night the scenes played out again and again before me, like a film that kept going back to the beginning each time it reached the credits.

Chapter Seven

Day Two

It had been a terrible night. The bed was hard, while the straps running down to the pulley restricted my movement, and the others made more noise than a crowd at St James' Park football stadium. But what really kept me awake were Alfred's haunting cries; screams of pain, shouts for help. They echoed in my head long after he had stopped. Dark figures whispered by his bed. In the semi-dark, I was glad Joe was between us.

It was seven-thirty and the first cup of tea had already been brought around. Several patients had gone to the washroom for a shave and wash before breakfast. I decided to join them so unstrapped the waistband, put on slippers, picked up my toilet bag and set off down the ward. I might have eaten first if I'd known I was to be greeted by the sight of Joe's backside as I walked in the door. He was naked, washing at one of the sinks. I found a spare sink further along.

Breakfast consisted of cereal, boiled eggs and toast, with as much tea or coffee as you could drink. As with the meals the previous day, we dragged it out for as long as possible. But in the end there was no escape and each of us in turn drifted back to bed and our own solitary thoughts.

Shortly after ten o'clock I joined the three others who were due to go to physiotherapy. There was the tall Glaswegian, John from Fife and the wizened old chap who still didn't appear to have found his teeth. They had all been before so I followed them, up and down corridors, including one dash between buildings as we tried to avoid the heavy rainfall.

The physiotherapist was waiting and wasted no time in making them begin their little exercises, although two collapsed in a heap almost as soon as they'd started. She turned to me and I had to go through a description of my symptoms.

'Right, can I see how far you can bend ... this way ...'

She placed her hands on my body in order to tilt me gently in the direction she wanted, while stopping me from going further than required.

'And this way ...'

Round I went, one way then another, stretching, bending and swinging my arms in various directions. After a series of increasingly vigorous exercises, we stopped.

'Well ... you're certainly flexible. And you say you have a lot of pain?'

'In the small of my back and around my side,' I confirmed, pointing once more just to make sure she knew the area I was referring to.

She made me take off my dressing gown and pyjama top and lie on a raised bench, on which there was a thin mattress covered in black plastic. Two patients were doing little more than standing watching by this time, while somewhere behind me the third grunted away as he attempted his exercises. I lay face down as instructed and the physiotherapist placed her hands on the base of my neck and began to move them down my back, her fingers massaging and probing every inch, trying to read it like a blind person might use Braille.

'It's rather strange,' she said at last. 'You seem to have some hard nodules just underneath the surface. They may just be tight muscles.' She paused then added. 'I'm going to give you some heat treatment to loosen these up. Stay where you are and I'll move the infra-red lamps nearer.'

There followed the sound of wheels being rolled across the linoleum and a few moments later a mobile stand appeared by my side. I was highly sceptical this was going to help, but as the lamps warmed my back I thought it wasn't going to do me any harm. Pretty soon, I was sunbathing on the beach and drifted along in this happy state for about twenty minutes, until there was a click and the sun disappeared.

There was a cup of tea on my locker, but it had long since gone cold so I poured some water and caught up with little Nell. Life on traction turned out to be a routine of lying in bed waiting for the next meal, lying some more, waiting for visiting hours then just lying. Anything that provided a valid excuse for moving around was grabbed at.

My visitor that evening was from the Scottish country dance group. Elaine shared a flat in Jesmond with two other girls and announced she would be moving out at the end of the month. For years, the property had been rented by dancers and as such it provided a base for parties, a meeting place for coffee and a general gathering point for the thirty or so who were in the class, which was affiliated to Newcastle University. Her news planted an idea in my mind, which I tucked away to be explored at a later date.

When the night staff came on duty nearly all of us took off our straps and a similar scene to the previous night developed, with card games and television, followed by stories when tea arrived. As I lay afterwards I was already feeling I had been there for weeks. Just like the first night, Alfred started crying out, even though throughout the day he had been quiet, as if he hadn't been there at all.

Day Four

If you counted all the odd bits as halves, which they virtually were anyway, then there were 240 tiles on the ward's ceiling. There were 12 windows, each with 8 panes so that made 96 panes in all. 14 beds equalled 56 bed legs, and if every patient drank 7 cups of tea each day then, by the end of the week, they had consumed 686 cups between them.

Day Five

I had heard earlier in the morning that he was arriving at twelve, and right on the stroke of noon I saw him. He was a small, elderly man who hesitated at the entrance for several moments, peering through thick spectacles up and down the ward.

I followed his gaze. Men, who had only moments before been reading, talking or listening to the radio on their headphones, were all asleep. Next to me, Joe was snoring loudly under his copy of *The Sun*. It was as I, too, looked at the unconscious figures, as I saw our new arrival's gaze fall upon me, and his frail legs propel him in a direction that could end at no other place than my bed, only then did I realise I had been set up once more.

'How are you today?' said the minister.

We covered my health, work, family, where I lived and touched on religion. Between every subject he paused to stare around the ward. The snoring was far worse than during the night when everyone actually was asleep. Joe's newspaper was almost being blown up in the air and I had to hide a smile at his performance.

It wasn't that I minded talking to the minister, it was just that he obviously had a set time for each ward, and as I was the only one 'awake' I was getting the full benefit. Also, I suppose part of me felt I wasn't 'one of the men' and was determined that, should the opportunity arise again, I would (shame on me) play along like the others.

Eventually, there was nothing more two complete strangers could say to each other, so the old gentleman wished me a speedy recovery and made his way slowly out of the ward. As on the other day, patients suddenly awoke from the deepest of slumbers. Books and newspapers were resumed and conversations restarted, as if they had never been interrupted.

Day Eight

It was Monday morning and the specialist was about to make his weekly round. In preparation for this, those of us who were able to get up, which was everyone except Alfred, had been instructed to stand by our beds so that if the specialist wanted to carry out an examination he could do so easily. Just before the visit a nurse rushed up and down, making sure locker doors were shut, everything was generally tidy and patients were actually there.

'It's like being in the bloody navy,' growled Joe. 'They'll be inspecting kit next and all those who don't pass will have their weights doubled as punishment.'

A few minutes later the group appeared at the entrance; doctors, nurses, the sister and, in the middle, the man who had examined me at the flat. Since entering hospital, I had discovered he was a rheumatologist. He stopped in front of the first patient and the accompanying staff gathered around so that the poor man was surrounded.

Eventually, they moved on and little by little came nearer, until I was the one standing in the centre. The specialist read my chart and asked how I was feeling. I had had an attack just before coming into hospital and they had fallen into a routine, so I wasn't expecting another one for a week or so. For the last seven days I had been perfectly well, and when this fact was relayed there was much bobbing of heads. The treatment was working.

'Good,' he said and moved on.

I sat down, letting out my breath in a long sigh, not having appreciated how tense the visit had made me. I wasn't really paying attention any more to what was being said, when suddenly a comment made me listen intently. Joe had just been told he could go home the next day. It hadn't occurred to me that he might leave before me and, although pleased for him, his imminent departure made me feel lonelier than ever.

The group moved on. The old sailor looked over and winked and I gave him the thumbs up. I wished more than ever I could go home as well. Had it been only a week? It felt as if someone had been pouring sand into the ward clock. Mam and Dad came that evening. They were on smiling terms with several of the patients by now, and very pleased by the specialist's comments.

Day Nine

It was early morning and time to join the others in the washroom. After I had washed and had breakfast I would have my daily session with the physiotherapist, who was still trying to rid me of the 'hard nodules'. Swinging my legs over the side of the bed, I stretched my feet down so that they made little indentations in the soft material of my slippers. There was no particular hurry. Something reached out and touched my subconscious ... and made me lift my head.

Alfred was staring at me with such piercing eyes I was rooted instantly where I sat. Clear blue eyes, the drugged glaze that had been there since the previous week thrown off in a moment of brilliant perception. The ward and all its beds faded, as if we were no longer a part of it, and I became aware of nothing outside Alfred's face and those blue whirlpools that sucked me nearer and nearer.

I wanted to get up, to go to the washroom where Joe and the others would be sharing a joke and enjoying a moment's freedom. But the intensity of Alfred's stare held even my breath motionless. What was he seeing? Death enveloped him as surely as those crisp, white hospital sheets, which he no longer had the strength to lift.

For the first time I saw the man. He was no longer someone to glance upon with curiosity in daytime, a person to be fearful of during the night. The lines in his face were not all caused by age. I had always thought his eyes were grey. They had always appeared this colour. But they were really so very blue. Still he held me and I felt ... stripped and helpless, as if all my weaknesses and frailties were reflected in those eyes.

Then Alfred closed them and moaned. When he opened his eyes again they had taken on the familiar dull grey and he wasn't seeing me anymore. I was free. But instead of rushing I walked away slowly, looking back constantly over my shoulder. Upon reaching the washroom, the others were just as I knew they would be, and only then did I realise I hadn't put on my slippers or picked up any toiletries.

Joe left the ward later that morning and there was a great deal of shaking of hands, good wishes and promises of keeping in touch. The relief on his face was evident to all and I wasn't the only one wishing that he was going, although a few others did leave that day. By lunchtime the ward had taken on a desolate feel and I felt empty along with it.

As the days passed I had become much more tuned into the real feelings of the men, and behind the façade of humour and jokes there was an underlying tension created by ill-health, pain and inactivity. A few nights earlier two patients had almost come to blows over a mug of tea and the atmosphere had turned unpleasant for a while.

Day Ten

This time I was prepared. I had overheard that today was the turn of the Irish priest. All morning I kept careful watch and shortly before twelve the men put down their newspapers and turned off radios. I moved down in the bed and just before closing my eyes caught a glimpse of a tall figure in black standing at the entrance. Unlike the previous occasions, the ward went deathly silent. I thought this might be a new ploy, so lay very still.

Several minutes went by. There wasn't a sound. I resisted the urge to peep and continued to lie as motionless as possible. More time passed. In the end it seemed to me that the situation was becoming ridiculous. The priest had obviously realised there was no one awake and not even come into the ward. There had certainly been no footsteps.

Why, oh why, oh why did I do it? Of all the prattish things I could have done at that particular moment, what I actually did had to be the king of prattish options. Did I continue to lie quietly? After all, it wasn't unpleasant. Did I open both eyes, stretch my arms and pretend I had just woken up? Oh no. These simple actions would have been nowhere near embarrassing enough.

Like some demented version of Marty Feldman, I opened

one eye to stare around the ward ... and looked up into the face of the priest standing above me. Boy was he mad. I don't know how long he had been by the bed, but he was wringing the life out of the hat held in his hands, no doubt wishing it was my neck.

There was no way out. I lay there, one eye open, the other shut and withered under his glare. I thought about closing the eye quickly and pretending that ... Well, what? It was useless. My guilt was plain. With the greatest reluctance, as if it had nothing whatsoever to do with anything going on around it, my other eye opened slowly.

Still, neither of us spoke. I stole a glance at his hat and suddenly felt closer to God.

'How are you?'

The question was not so much spoken as spat through clenched teeth. Now looking at his face again, I found that I had lost the power of speech. He was a big man and in my horizontal position he looked altogether too big. In what has to be the feeblest of replies, I merely nodded meekly. More silence followed.

'Is there anything ... I can get you?'

The question appeared to cause the priest great internal torment, because the hat was now being wrung permanently out of shape, and I suspected strongly that uncharitable thoughts were going through his mind. I shook my head.

'Well ...' he said after a long pause. 'I'll be going then.'

And with one last painful squeeze of his hat, he turned around and walked out of the ward.

Day Thirteen

It was a Saturday night, so visiting time was earlier and, with friends and family gone, most of us sat in the television room. The card games had lost their gloss since Joe's departure. I stayed a few minutes longer than the others and when I entered the ward they were all standing just beyond the doorway. I heard the sound and stood, motionless and silent like the rest. It was a sound that froze the soul; that of a body refusing to let go of life.

'What's that?' someone whispered.

'It's Alfred,' came a reply.

'It's the death rattle,' said another.

Our little group stood quietly, strangers thrown together by fate. No one moved for several minutes then a nurse appeared from behind the curtains that had been pulled around Alfred's bed and walked to the exit. It seemed to break the spell and we moved silently to lay down our mugs on the trolley. Alfred died a few hours later.

I never knew anything about him other than he ended his time on earth two beds away from mine, and that he had a wife, who would sit during visiting time, holding his hand. I didn't speak to him, nor ever heard him talk; only his cries and shouts. But I knew I would always remember, right until I lie on my own death bed, the look that passed between us.

Day Fifteen

It was Monday and I could hardly sit still. The specialist was due to make his round and I was hoping he would allow me to go home. We lined up, just like the previous Monday, and a nurse ran around checking that everything, and everybody, was ready. There was an even larger group that morning and it seemed to take an age to move up the ward but, eventually, there he was.

'How have you been feeling?'

'Fine, thank you,' I replied.

'Good. Would you please lift up your top so that we can see your back?'

I turned around, lifted my pyjama top and the doctors crowded around as if it was the most interesting back in the world. I felt the specialist's hands move gently up and down my spine.

'Your back is weak. Take up swimming when you get out of hospital.'

I turned to face him again.

'Would you walk towards the entrance, just as naturally as you can.'

Well, I thought, that's no problem. They parted so I had a clear path beyond the ends of the beds, while the other patients watched, like owls around a mouse hole. It struck me how I had suddenly become the centre of attention. Clearing my throat, I tucked in my top and set off.

Piece of cake. Back at the flats by coffee time.

I had only taken three steps when my right leg developed a slight twitch. I ignored it, but a few steps further on I found myself unexpectedly veering to the left. I counteracted this by leaning to the right, which made the twitch worse. By the time I was half-way down the ward I was beginning to lose control of both legs, while my head was displaying a never-before-seen nervous tic.

I couldn't believe it. I had been walking perfectly well for the past twenty-three years, barring some uncertainty in my early months and the very occasional Saturday night. Now that all I had to do to gain my freedom was walk a few yards in front of a crowd of people, I was losing control of every limb.

Increasing the pace made everything worse and by the time I reached the entrance I was lurching and staggering around so badly that I almost fell over completely. However, walking back towards the specialist, when I could see him scrutinising my every move, was even worse. If I blew this I could be on traction for goodness knows how long. I might never get out and end up an old man, still on the ward, constantly retelling a joke about an officer and a camel.

Shaking my head (not a good decision) to steel myself for the return journey, I set off with the level of determination needed to run a marathon. As I finally approached my own bed I was a shaking wreck of jerking limbs and twitching features. It probably wouldn't have surprised anyone if I had started dribbling.

We stood in silence for a long time while the specialist looked at me, clearly very disappointed. How could I tell Mam she would be visiting me in hospital for years to come? Eventually, he dispelled the tension that hung in the air alongside the smell of disinfectant.

'Excellent. Well, I don't see any reason why you can't go home tomorrow.'

Chapter Eight

The telephone rang for a long time before it was picked up and I could hear Val on the other end.

'Hang on,' she said, when I had explained the reason for my call.

Her voice carried clearly down the line as she shouted to Andreana, who I took to be in another room.

'I've got Philip on the line. What do you think of him?'

There was a pause then Andreana could be heard rather hesitantly calling back.

'Philip? Well ... he's alright.'

'No, no,' said Val, taken aback. 'I mean what do you think of him to share the flat?'

It was all settled. Elaine was moving out at the end of February and I would start paying rent from 1st March, moving in whenever suited me after that. I had come out of hospital the previous day and was signed off sick until the following week.

That night, before getting undressed, I sat down on the blanket box to think. Dad had made it years earlier. He was good at woodwork and to make extra money he built dolls' houses, toy forts and garages, which he would sell to neighbours in the block. Somewhere underneath me, buried by a pile of neatly folded spare blankets, was my childhood teddy bear.

When I had been young, Mam had apparently been worried that I might swallow Teddy's eyes, so Dad was given the task of pulling them out, which took about five minutes with the biggest pair of pliers in his tool box. She had sewn back in the eyes with black thread, and from that moment Teddy had always looked upon the world with a rather startled expression. Mam must have had some thread left over, because she sewed up his mouth. Perhaps it was to stop him ever telling of the terrible deed carried out.

When you grow up in a place, rooms trigger so many memories, and bedrooms in particular are the keepers of extreme emotions. It's where you are when you're ill, where you keep your toys and possessions, where Mam reads you stories when you're small.

When I was eight, the gas mains burst outside during the night and, because I slept under the window and it was open, I was well and truly gassed by the time Mam came to wake me up. She still sent me to school as she was worried there could be an explosion. It was nearly Christmas and I was meant to be in the school play. It was the only time in my life that I was going to be on stage. The opportunity to be King Herod never came my way again.

I was certain that the fortnight on traction had not cured me of my recent ill-health, but could see no other way forward for the moment. This treatment was over and could be crossed off the list.

Following the specialist's comment that I should take up swimming, I had purchased trunks earlier in the day and planned to visit the local baths the next morning, but I had the feeling of being on the wrong train and unable to get off.

I sighed, stood up and started to undress. Since starting work and earning money I had bought my own clothes, but until then Mam had purchased everything. That's how things were. The main considerations were that clothes were cheap and hard-wearing, rather than being comfortable or even warm, while fashion was not a word ever to be heard mentioned. The Co-op, bless them, sold a wide variety of items made of nylon.

Never mind the Milky Bar Kid, I was the Nylon Kid of the North: socks, shirts, jumpers, my raincoat. Even my underpants were nylon and when, at night, I slid between those nylon sheets on the bed ... I did so with extreme caution and trepidation.

I looked at the water and hesitated for one very good reason. I couldn't swim. Once before, I had stood on that spot at the edge of the local swimming pool. There had been a line of us, all skinny thirteen-year-old lads. I was second from the front, behind my best friend at that time, a boy named John Ridley. We had been ordered into the row by the PE teacher and were to jump, one at a time, into the water. At least that was the plan.

'In you go, Ridley,' shouted the teacher, standing a few yards away from the group.

Like most PE teachers of the time, he always used our surname and spoke as if he were extremely angry at something, though we never knew what.

'Please, sir. I can't swim, sir,' said John.

'Not at all?'

'Not at all, sir.'

'Paris. In you go.'

John, who was a good deal shorter than me, wasted no time in running around to the relative safety of the back of the queue.

'I'm sorry, sir. I can't swim either,' I said.

'In you go, Paris. Don't waste time.'

'But I can't swim a stroke, sir.'

'PARIS! GET IN THE WATER.'

There was nothing else for it. I took the small step needed to take me to the edge. We were at the deep end. Behind me, the others watched. Some, no doubt, with glee; others probably just grateful they weren't at the front.

Jumping into the water with a great splash I floated as gently to the bottom as a brick thrown out of an aeroplane. Everything went quiet. All I could hear was the panic within my head. After several moments of waving my arms and legs about and not actually going anywhere, I thrust my feet against the bottom and seconds later broke the surface. Above my gasps and desperate splashing, I could hear the teacher shouting.

'Alright, Paris. Get out and let ....'

I sank to the bottom with even less dignity than the first time. This bizarre one-sided conversation continued, with the teacher becoming increasingly agitated, though doing nothing to get me out, and my calls for help becoming ever more frantic. The line of boys broke up and gathered around the edge to watch my plight, with the delight that is particularly to be found in the male species at that age. Eventually, by chance, I surfaced near to the edge, exhausted and totally wretched. Two friends reached down, grabbed an arm each, and pulled me out.

The experience gave me a hate and fear of water, which was why that morning, at the age of twenty-three, I stood, watched and did nothing. It was ridiculous. Children who looked about eight were swimming up and down the pool with ease. I went to the shallow end and gingerly climbed down the steps then, after a pause to pluck up more courage, walked along the side until almost out of my depth.

All the while I had been observing how other people

moved in the water. Squeezing as much air into my lungs as possible, I trusted myself to fate and swam up and down the pool as if it had been a regular occurrence all my life. Well, in truth I did a gentle breast stroke, always keeping within reach of the side. But to me it was a minor miracle. The fear disappeared within minutes and after completing many laps I realised there was one thing to thank the specialist for.

The next Monday I was back at my desk in the costing department at the HMSO factory. As I sat with the production figures for the latest telephone directory to be despatched, Joe and Alfred, lying in the ward on traction, seemed to be events that had happened so very long ago. It's strange how a few days away from something could create that illusion.

As for the numerous enquiries from colleagues about my health, I thought it best just to answer I was very well and leave it at that. Ironically, I started swimming in my lunch hour and was so enthusiastic that by the end of the week a small group from the office also came along.

It was the Tuesday of the following week when the attack happened again. The morning passed in a haze of pain and sickness, spent between my bed and the bathroom. Mam kept appearing at the bedroom door, looking old and frail; helplessness etched into her face.

She had telephoned the office to let them know I wouldn't be in and the news had gone down like pork at a Bar Mitzvah. The telephone had been put down on her. Mam didn't deserve that. Around lunchtime I fell into a deep sleep, waking up later that evening. The search for a cure was about to start again in earnest.

The next day I went back to work and that weekend I

moved into the flat in Jesmond. A friend with a car helped move my few possessions, including the board from under my mattress. Though I didn't think it was doing any good, I was trying every possibility.

I had been to the flat many times and it had everything ... damp, dry rot, woodworm. The stairs leading down to the yard at the back were so unsafe they were almost unusable. But the place offered a sense of freedom and a social life I loved.

As the weeks passed work also became much better, for although I had further to travel each day I was moved to the production office. This made up the top part of what was essentially a two-deck structure, situated within the centre of the factory, quite removed from the tower block.

In charge of the office was Fred, one of life's true gentlemen. Small, bald and nearing retirement, he was far more interested in the first aid courses he taught than in anything to do with the production of telephone directories. I never saw Fred without a smile on his face, even in the midst of a crisis, and the atmosphere he generated around him was one of laughter and fun.

By this time I was swimming three or four times a week in order to strengthen my back, but the attacks of pain and sickness came with increasing frequency and, at the end of April, I was once more sitting in front of my GP. I wasn't quite sure what he would suggest, as he had already passed me into the hands of a specialist. But here I was, asking for his opinion again.

He checked my notes and examined me as if meeting for the first time. Then he sat down and fell silent for several moments. It appeared he was out of ideas. Across the table, the demigod had become a bloke in a crumpled brown suit.

'I think the muscles in your back are going into spasm,' he said. 'I'm going to give you a prescription for something that will stop them tightening up.'

I liked my GP. He was willing to keep trying something different and was on my side. I took the prescription and called in at the local chemist, where the pharmacist and I were becoming well-acquainted.

The medicine turned out to be a bottle of white stuff, which had the consistency of honey and tasted as I imagined cardboard would if it was in liquid form. That night I took two spoonfuls as instructed on the bottle and repeated the dose before going to work.

It hit me unexpectedly whilst I was sitting at my desk later in the morning. I leapt up cursing loudly, banging my knee painfully against the table and knocking over a half-finished cup of coffee on the latest production sheets. Fred glanced over from his desk, but before he could speak I was out of the room and running along the corridor, down the stairs, two, three, four at a time and out on to the factory floor like an express train emerging from a tunnel.

I was sprinting now. Beads of sweat breaking out on my brow, while people operating nearby machines watched in amazement as I flew past, disregarding completely the safety regulations regarding the forklift trucks, which roamed constantly like giant yellow beetles. Bursting through the double doors that connected the factory to the tower block, I almost knocked over the general manager before disappearing through a door marked with the figure of a little man. I just made it.

What the doctor hadn't warned me about was that the medicine could result in what was known locally as the 'squits'. These attacks were so sudden that for the next seven days people working on the shop floor thought I was training for the Great North Run, and there were several admiring comments at the speed achieved. Certainly, for this brief period, I claimed the title of the fastest moving civil servant in the entire service.

One evening, while standing in the bathroom at the flat in Jesmond and about to start into the second bottle of medicine, an unusual feeling of rebellion swept over me. I had the bottle in one hand, a spoon in the other and kept looking between the two. Then my eye was drawn to the toilet, just to my left.

In the end, I decided to miss out the middle man and emptied the entire contents into the bowl. There was a great feeling of satisfaction as my tormentor swirled around the pan and disappeared altogether from my life with an undignified glug.

Chapter Nine

People commented increasingly upon my weight loss and it was hardly surprising. Clothes hung on me as if they had been made for someone many times my size, while punching holes in belts became a common pastime. Even my kilt was slack and, while dancing, I was in danger of providing, unintentionally, the answer to one of life's great mysteries.

I was convinced that getting rid of the medicine had been the right thing to do. But I could hardly tell my GP that his last attempt had been disposed of down the toilet, and I felt I had effectively removed myself from the game. The question was ... what to do now?

Months earlier, I had written out a list of possible alternatives: acupuncturist, osteopath, faith healer ... Some of the names meant nothing to me and I only had a vague idea of what the others stood for. With no medical knowledge whatsoever, all I could base my decisions on was that it was *my body*, and somehow, everything said to me so far just didn't seem right.

I chose the osteopath, partly in the hope that he might agree that there was nothing wrong with my spine, so this idea could be crossed off the list completely, and partly because I knew people went to see osteopaths. It felt a safer option.

This was why, a few weeks later, I found myself lying on a table in the front room of a strange house, my knees somewhere up by my ears, a woman I'd never met before holding down my shoulders and some chap built like a brick outhouse grappling with my lower region. The fact that he kept telling me it wouldn't hurt did not put my mind at rest.

Upon arrival I had explained my problem to the osteopath and his assistant and, following an examination, was told there were three discs out of place, one of which was, without any shadow of a doubt, the cause of my pain. This was not going to plan.

'But the pain is not there, in my spine, it's here,' I said pointing around my side, with probably more than a hint of the hopelessness I felt at having so little power over my destiny.

'Pain can be felt in a different part of the body from the site of the trouble,' assured the osteopath. 'Yes, yes, the problem is clear enough. We'll soon have you sorted.'

I was on the wrong train once more, with the conductor insisting I go to the end of the line before being able to return and board the right one. All the while I was trundling in the opposite direction to where I wanted to go.

'Let's get these first two discs back in place to start with. The worst one will need a course of traction, as well as manipulation,' he said.

I pointed out I had been given two weeks of continuous traction and this hadn't helped at all.

'The main issue I have with the traction people receive in hospitals is that the force used is too weak to do any good. No. No. Far too ineffective. What I use will be much greater.'

And so there I was, on the table.

'This won't hurt at all,' he said, rocking my legs and hips from side to side.

I didn't believe him and had my scream all prepared. I tried to distract my mind by looking at the assistant's breasts, which swayed gently above me, only inches from my face. (Actually, I couldn't see anything else as they completely filled my vision). Perhaps the trip wasn't entirely wasted. The osteopath was building up to the twist that would 'put the first disc back in place.'

Did he really know what he was doing? I had had no more than a word-of-mouth recommendation from somebody who knew someone who had their sciatica cured. Would I ever dance again? I might never even be able to walk. Despite the breasts, I was rapidly regretting this decision.

'I want you to relax completely.'

Rock ... rock.

'Let yourself go limp.'

Suddenly, the lower half of my body was twisted sharply to one side.

'There. Did you hear the disc click back in?'

I didn't, but nodded anyway in case he felt he had to do it again just for my benefit. I was about to get up.

'Now, we'll just do the other one.'

The same procedure followed. In truth, it didn't hurt, but neither did I hear any discs going back in, even though each time he said he could hear them clearly. Part of me felt I should pull the emergency cord, stop the train and get off. But I wasn't strong enough. I had nowhere near sufficient confidence to stand up and say, 'I think you're wrong and I'm not coming back.' Instead, I paid the bill and made another appointment.

One Sunday not long after this first encounter with the osteopath I woke with a huge desire to play the pipes, which may be difficult for those less inclined towards this grand instrument to understand. The Jesmond flat was only a few minutes' walk from the Great North Road, and on the other side of this was the Town Moor, a massive expanse of grassland well-known throughout the area for hosting the annual 'Hoppings', which was said to be Europe's largest travelling fair.

After breakfast I picked up my sturdy black case and set off for what I assumed would be a good morning's piping. No hysterical shopkeepers to bother me this time. Instead, there was the usual assortment of joggers and people walking dogs. In the distance a couple of men were flying a model aeroplane, and beyond them a small herd of cattle grazed quietly. I chose my spot, well away from everyone.

The air was fresh (well, relatively speaking), the sky was clear and I felt there was nothing more on earth I would rather do than play a few jigs, reels and slow airs in the open. It was a great day to be a piper.

It didn't take long to tune the instrument and I was soon into the first of four slow airs. I played for about ten minutes, drawing out the music by constantly swapping between tunes then stopped for a rest. You don't really know silence until someone nearby stops playing the pipes. Wanting to enjoy the moment to its full, and also in need of a breather, I tucked the pipes under my arm and stood quite still, feeling rather pleased with myself and at peace with the world.

However, just as I was being so harmonious with my surroundings, a strange, uncomfortable sensation began to creep over me; the sort of thing you experience when you've seen a movement in the corner of a darkened room that is meant to be empty. And there wasn't quite the silence there should have been.

Yes, there was definitely something ... breathing. I could hear heavy breathing. On the back of my left hand, which was hanging down by my side, I felt warm, moist air blow across the skin and heard a deep, rasping, inhuman noise that made the hairs on the back of my neck rise. Had my playing disturbed the hideous Lampton Worm?

With a thumping heart I turned around slowly ... to face seven cows, which were gathering around. Now I'm sure they are very nice animals, but there weren't many of them in Gateshead so this encounter wasn't something I was used to. And they're rather large. The nearest one rubbed a dripping nose against the end of my base drone.

I was forced backwards and only managed with some difficulty to rescue my case before I was separated from it completely. The cows were forming a circle, with me in the middle. It perhaps wasn't General Custer's last stand, but I wasn't at all happy at this turn of events. With the pipes still under my arm and the case in the other hand, I started to walk away, thinking to leave them behind.

My new-found bovine friends fell into an orderly line and followed. I walked faster. They walked faster. I broke into a slight jog and the cows simply trotted along, easily keeping pace. This was ludicrous. I had heard of the Pied Piper. At this moment I caught sight of a jogger who had stopped dead in his tracks and was standing about ten yards away, watching the spectacle before him with one of the most astonished expressions I've ever seen. I called over.

'Have you any suggestions on how to get rid of these?'

The jogger didn't even shake his head in reply. We passed him by. I was running now, the pipes bouncing around dangerously and the case banging painfully against my leg. For anyone who has never raced a cow, take my word for it, you cannot outpace them. I pressed on, wondering what Val would say when I returned to the flat with a small heard of Friesians.

After a while I glanced behind and saw that two of the cows had lost interest and were standing, watching. We carried on and another animal bowed out, then another. I was bloody knackered. Eventually, there remained one cow, whose bogeys were still hanging from the end of my base drone. It had obviously fallen helplessly in love with the pipes, but at that moment we passed a very succulent patch of grass and she gave up the chase as well.

I quickly left them behind and eventually came to a stop, threw my case on the ground and bent over, gasping. My urge to play had, not surprisingly, gone. When I finally caught my breath, I put the pipes away and headed sadly back to the flat for a cup of tea and a sit down. There had to be an easier instrument to play.

It wasn't long before I was once more with the osteopath, this time to start the course of traction. As I was taking off my shoes and coat I outlined my symptoms yet again.

'Stand in front of me,' he said when I was in my shirt and trousers.

He faced me and placed a large and powerful hand on my right side, so that his fingers were on my back and his thumb was round the front, then he squeezed.

'Does this hurt?'

It didn't.

'Well,' he said, 'it can't be your kidney.'

I lay on the black plastic-covered table and his assistant fixed retraining straps about my chest and under my arms, then a second set around my waist. These led to a pulley system at the bottom of the bench, only instead of loose weights there was an electrically driven wheel. When I was ready (hardly the right word) she turned on the machine.

'You'll feel the straps pulling,' said the osteopath, who had been standing nearby while I was being prepared. 'The force will gradually increase until it reaches the level I've set. We'll keep you on it for about twenty minutes. What they do at the hospital is not any use,' he said, repeating his previous comments, 'not any use at all.'

Indeed, as he spoke, I could feel myself being pulled strongly, and if my top half had not been held I would simply have been dragged down the table. As none of us were going anywhere, I thought I would do some digging.

'Just what exactly do you think the problem is?'

'Well, let me show you,' he replied, full of enthusiasm for the opportunity to talk about his favourite subject.

He walked over to a cabinet in the corner of the room and came back moments later with a large medical book, which he proceeded to flick through.

'You see ... (flick, flick) ... discs don't really slip, as people so often say. What they do is bulge. But because they are very sticky, once they move out of position we have to relieve the normal pressure on the spine in order to manipulate them back again, hence the traction. Here it is.'

He turned the book around and held it so that, from my horizontal position, I could see a page that contained a diagram showing a spine with a bulging disc. I was glad it was only a drawing.

'This is what you've got, so you've nothing to worry about. It's just a case of relieving the pressure so the disc can be put back to where it should be. Yes, yes, nothing to worry about at all.'

I couldn't decide whether he was really convinced or if this was just the 'professional confidence' he felt he should convey. No room for doubt in the patient's mind. This was the correct diagnosis and anything that had gone before was simply to be ignored as if someone else's opinion couldn't possibly be correct.

Nevertheless, the osteopath was a friendly chap and to pass the time he told stories of his adventures as a young man. The assistant smiled at all the right places, even though she had no doubt heard the tales before.

He was funny and I actually quite liked the guy. It was just that I was as confident he was wrong as he appeared to be in believing what he said. The osteopath threw in bits of advice about maintaining a good posture and how best to lift heavy or awkward objects, with some words of caution about taking a bath.

'There is no real support for your back when sitting in the bath,' he said, 'so don't lie there for long periods thinking it will help.'

I assured him I would, from that point onwards, only ever take quick baths.

'Can you feel your back getting warm?' asked the assistant.

'No. I can't. What would that mean?' I asked.

'That it was working,' she replied.

When my time was up the assistant pressed a switch and the pulling sensation eased slowly until the straps went slack. They both helped to untie me. I didn't feel any different from when I had walked in half an hour earlier.

'We'll see you again soon?' he said.

Pull the cord. Pull the cord. Stop the train and get off. GET OFF.

'How about a week on Saturday?' I replied.

* * *

81

The summer wore on. I went swimming so often I was never free of the smell of chlorine, slept with the unyielding board under my mattress until I forgot what it was like to sink into a soft bed, and continued to be pulled apart by the osteopath so that I ended up with stretch marks all the way down my back. The attacks of pain and sickness continued with increasing regularity, while checking my weight had become a rather masochistic pastime.

However, I pushed the whole business out of my mind and carried on with dancing and enjoying the social life that went with living in the flat. At work, I was often saved by Fred. Many times he let me go saying, with that cheerful sing-song voice of his, 'Well, you're no good to me here, so you might as well go to bed. Go on, get yourself away.' Sometimes I was too ill to travel to Jesmond so I went back to the block of flats, where my bed was always ready.

I stopped playing the pipes. It was the one activity that always brought on an attack. I assumed it was caused by the pressure of blowing the bag, but beyond that didn't have any theories. It was a sad day. Polishing the drones for the last time I thought about the occasion a few years earlier when I had been offered a holiday in Holland.

While a teenager, I had taken a bus every summer from Newcastle's Haymarket station to Wooler, in order to spend a week with my Great Auntie Mary. She was Mam's aunt, who had never married, and of all my many relatives was the one I was closest to, despite the huge age difference. On one visit I took the pipes and on a particularly fine day carried the case all the way to the top of nearby Humbledon Hill. Not the easiest walk I've ever done.

Once rested, I got them out and started to play. What an unforgettable experience. There had been no one in sight when I began, but after a while a couple of hikers came along. They sat down to listen and when I stopped we got talking. They lived in Amsterdam and were astounded to find a bloke playing at the top of a hill in the otherwise deserted countryside! We got on so well that they gave me their address and said I should stay with them. I went the following year and had a great time.

More memories came back as I wrapped the chanter in a clean yellow duster; like the time the band had played at a particular garden fête. We met about half an hour before we were due to play, and two members duly set off to find someone who could tell us where to tune up away from visitors.

They found a woman with a clipboard who seemed to be organising everyone around her and so explained our requirements. However, the request had the unexpected result of making her extremely angry. She turned on the two pipers, saying:

'Really. Really. This is not good enough. You've known about this event for months and you leave it until the last minute to tune up!'

I suppose she had a point.

Having tucked away my spare reeds, I closed the lid and flicked the catches to lock the case. An old friend had gone and I had no idea when we might meet again.

By the September, the osteopath had decided that traction and manipulation were not working and that I needed an operation to remove the disc he was convinced was causing the pain. He even had the name of the surgeon to whom he wanted to refer to me.

I was saved from going any further down this route by the fact that I had to return to Watford for my final year at college. On Sunday, 19th September, I left the flat in Jesmond for the last time, said farewell to Mam and Dad at Newcastle station and boarded a train to Kings Cross. At least for the moment I was on a real train, going in the right direction.

As we travelled south, passing through York, where I had so enjoyed the previous summer, I pondered my next course of action.

Chapter Ten

Fate is a funny old thing and it so happened that the lodger who had replaced me had only just moved away, so my old room at Gammons Lane was vacant once more, and I arrived there late in the afternoon. The bedroom was exactly as it had been, with its little table and chair, its cheery gas fire and the enormous bed. The latter looked as though it had grown even higher.

Paul was still occupying the room downstairs. At weekends the routine in the house changed and Mr Wilcox brought breakfast and lunch, so evenings were free for everyone. Paul and I, who were a similar age, went out for a meal. He updated me on what had been happening during my absence. He also knew Rose, and apparently the folk dance class was going as strongly as ever. I told him about my deteriorating health and he listened with a grave expression.

'What are you going to do now?' he asked.

'Well, I thought I would go to the top and work down,' I answered. 'I've decided to try and get an appointment with a Harley Street specialist, though I don't know how you go about such a thing, and I dread to imagine what it will cost.'

On the journey from Newcastle, I had again written out the list of options as far as I could visualise them. 'Osteopath' was well crossed out, but the potentials still contained 'acupuncture', 'faith health', plus a few others, and now that I would be living close to London again I had added a new possibility.

Even a printing student from Gateshead had heard of Harley Street specialists. What these people were experts in I hadn't a clue, but I assumed they were near the top of the medical tree. Paul didn't have much idea either. When we returned to our lodgings he brought out his chess set and thrashed me decisively at the game for the remainder of the evening. He always did.

Although students were not given any set work for their time spent in industry, I had intended to maintain a certain level of studying. This had simply not happened and going back to college the next day was a shock to the grey cells.

I relaxed that first evening by going to the dance class, where Rose, Babs and the others I had got to know during my first year at college were still casting off, turning their partners and going back-to-back, as well as they ever had. There were a few comments about how much weight I had lost, but most people merely said they were pleased to see me again.

Babs was in her usual good form and, during the interval, while we munched on slices of Bertha's bread-and-butter pudding, she expounded on the disadvantages of growing old as she checked her lipstick in a small hand mirror.

'You know,' she said to the little group sitting around, 'when I was a young girl I would often look at older women going around with heavy make-up on their faces and think, "Ugh, when I get to that age I'll never be like that." The problem is, now I am that age, I'm probably wearing more than any of them ever did!'

With that profound statement on the frailty of human nature, she began to laugh and we all joined in. One of the dancers was a physiotherapist and before the second half of the class began I outlined my problem to her. Could she recommend someone in Harley Street? She gave me a name and I wrote down the details just as Ivan, the caller, was getting everyone back on the floor.

The next day, I set about making an appointment and several weeks later I was once more throwing the dice in the game of quest for a cure. As I walked into the London surgery on that brilliantly clear October day, I entered a world where wealth was accepted as normal, and the pattern around the china teacups met up properly all the way around.

It was not the trainers of a printing student that the deep, mauve carpet was used to having upon it. I suspected that the pictures on the walls were not reproductions and the huge reception desk was real mahogany down to the last grain. The vision of beauty who greeted me flashed a dazzling smile, took my details and asked me to sit down, indicating, with a skilfully manicured hand, a black leather armchair situated between two enormous plants.

What I was about to receive, which was half an hour, was going to cost thirty pounds. This was a significant amount to me and if the specialist suggested further treatment it was likely to be well out of my league financially. I shifted uneasily in the armchair, feeling as out of place as I had ever felt, although in fairness I had received far less friendly welcomes in my life than the one just given.

Not many minutes had passed when the receptionist informed me that if I followed the corridor to the double doors at the end I would find the doctor's room. I returned her smile, but mine was a poor match so I set off, knocking moments later on one of the huge double doors before opening it.

For all her professional appearance the receptionist had

been a bit premature in sending me along because the previous patient was just leaving. He was a very elderly chap, walking with considerable difficulty, his breathing coming in great gasps. I stood to one side, holding open the heavy door and glancing about to see if there was a walking stick or a Zimmer nearby. I couldn't spot anything, so as he reached the doorway was just about to take his elbow to help steer him through, when he said:

'Well, come in, come in. Tell me what the problem is.'

The room was vast and the high, ornate ceiling looked down on to a collection of antique furniture, nests of delicately turned tables, elegant ladder-back chairs, plus a large bookcase full of old, and no doubt very rare, books. Even the screen in the corner for modest souls to change behind had its intricately embroidered material encased by a gilt frame. The only modern item, as far as I could see, was the all-too-familiar black plastic-covered table in the centre of the room.

The specialist wasted no time and got me to explain my illness in detail, stopping me at times with a searching question, particularly about the various diagnoses and treatments I had received already. Then he asked me to take off my shirt and we went through the bending, twisting, prodding exercises I knew so well. He did actually seem to be listening and I was impressed by his approach.

When I had bent over, swung my arms, twisted around and generally done everything bar cartwheels, he told me to lie face down on the table. Feeling up and down my spine with his fingers, he asked me to let him know if I felt pain at any particular point. I didn't.

'You can put on your shirt,' he said, walking over to the bookcase in the corner and standing with his back to me. I went to the chair where my shirt, shoes and coat had been left and started to dress. From behind, he looked even older and his head and shoulders drooped as if a lifetime of trying to fit together complex jigsaws had worn him down. Perhaps he had seen too many pictures with missing pieces. Yet, despite this, the specialist had a deep commanding voice, which resounded throughout the room as if he was a Shakespearean actor.

'There's certainly nothing wrong with your back.'

I heard him say it. He hadn't turned around, but I had definitely heard him say it. I just couldn't quite believe the words.

'I'm sorry,' I said.

'There's nothing wrong with your back, at least not with your spine.'

Nothing wrong with my spine! Could I have that in writing?

'What do you think it is?' I asked.

I had always thought that when I heard the right answer, I would know it. This assumption may have been completely incorrect, but it's what had kept me searching.

'I don't know,' he said, turning around to face me.

Well, it was an honest reply if nothing else and the old gent had gone up a lot in my estimation, since I had tried to find his Zimmer for him. The problem was that the other options on my list seemed to pale by comparison to a Harley Street specialist. So where did I go from here?

'Have you ever had a barium meal?'

I shook my head, not mentioning fish fingers. It wasn't the proper moment.

'I don't know if it will reveal the answer, but the problem might be intestinal. It's what I would suggest you try.'

And that was it. Bang on thirty minutes, which I reckoned

to be a feat almost equal to any medical skill. I left him to his next patient, whose feet were sticking out from behind one of the plants surrounding the armchair.

On the train back to Watford I considered my options. Money was severely limited and I had been brought up only to buy what you could afford to pay for. The thought of going into debt ... The other slight issue, of course, was that I had absolutely no idea how you went about getting a barium meal or what such a thing was.

As I walked from the station to Gammons Lane it seemed the only route available was to go to the GP with whom I had signed on again, following my recent return to college. The following week, I was sitting in front of him, explaining what had happened during the last year.

Then we sat in silence. Perhaps he had just had a terrible night, or had told the person before me that they only had months to live. I was sure the GP faced terrible situations on a daily basis, of which I had no concept whatsoever. But even when I had developed glandular fever during my first year at college, which seemed a fair enough reason to me to visit the surgery, I had been greeted with the same unfriendly reception.

The school playgrounds of Gateshead had taught me early on in life that the characteristics we each possess that make some people feel a kinship towards us will be the very qualities that create hostility in others. Maybe he simply didn't like Geordies.

'So ... you want me to send you for a barium meal?'

'I would be very grateful ...'

There was another silence. I got the feeling he thought I was wasting his time. He obviously wasn't keen, but eventually broke the silence.

'Alright. I'll arrange for you to have one at Watford General Hospital. They'll be in touch.'

On 5th November, I celebrated my birthday. I was twenty-four. The battle to stay on top of my studies became more difficult, and an increasing number of evenings and weekends were spent completing assignments. My other concern was that the college demanded a high attendance level at classes. I spoke to my course tutor, Francis Goode, and he told me that as long as I kept on top of the work, I needn't worry about missing lessons if it was because of ill-health.

It was the beginning of December when I returned to the surgery to find out the results of the barium meal. The X-ray itself had been a straightforward affair, the main drawback being not able to eat for some time before the test. I sat quietly in the waiting room surrounded by the familiar posters and leaflets, and thought again how different it was from its bustling, overflowing equivalent in Gateshead.

I felt pretty rough as I had been sick all the previous day. The attacks were now occurring almost every week, and a feeling of urgency was never far away. Time was running out. Waiting for appointments, tests, being put on the wrong train, then starting again ... they were all using up time. It had been more than eighteen months since I had woken with a dull ache in the small of my back. I needed a double six more than ever.

'Mr Paris. Mr Paris?'

The receptionist was calling to me. I looked up, a little startled from the sleepy state into which I had sunk without realising.

'The doctor will see you now.'

I walked along to his room, knocked, waited to hear 'enter'

and went in. He said nothing for a long while and the only sound was the tapping of his pencil on the desk.

'The results of your barium meal were negative. So there's nothing wrong with your intestine,' he said.

This wasn't a surprise as I hadn't thought there was. At the back of my mind, little warning bells were ringing and I didn't know why.

'You've seen a lot of doctors and specialists ... haven't you?'

I nodded.

'You've had several trips to your own GP, then the rheumatologist ...'

'Yes.'

'... and you've seen an osteopath and a Harley Street specialist, and now the results of the barium meal are negative ...'

The bells were ringing so loudly in my head that I was almost knocked off my seat.

Where was this going?

He told me.

'I think all this is being caused by your imagination. I'm going to put you on a course of Valium.'

He started to write out the prescription and I was too numb to react.

He thinks it's in my mind? Valium?

The prescription was a simple piece of paper; not a complex form with difficult questions to trip you up. It wasn't a garishly coloured offensive sheet, or something cut so delicately that you couldn't pick it up without destroying the pattern completely. It was just a black-and-white piece of paper, providing an easy black-and-white solution.

I had boarded many trains in this journey of mine and,

generally, I had known they were the wrong ones before I got on. But some journeys in life have to be made, even if we don't want to make them. What final destination would the Valium locomotive take me to? At what out-of-sight abandoned station did that line end? This was one train I wasn't prepared to board.

'No,' I said. 'It's not in my mind. I'm not taking it.'

There.

It was done.

I had eventually rebelled, said 'NO', and broken a lifetime of obedience; broken the lifetime of obedience that my parents had given, and their parents before them. So we sat in silence, looking at each other across his desk, irritation on one side and despair on the other. The game was over. He had made his offer and I had turned him down. There was nothing left for either of us to say. I stood up and walked out.

Chapter Eleven

At that age, I didn't really know anything about anything. I had signed on with a local doctors' practice on arriving in Watford, because that's what the college told the students to do. But I didn't know you could change your GP because you wanted to ... because you needed to ... so this particular option was not amongst my list of possible next moves as I walked away from the surgery.

I was in no mood to rejoin a class, so carried on and eventually entered Cassiobury Park. Autumn had long given way to winter and the trees were bare. A few leaves blew along the ground, but they were about my only companions that morning.

It was too cold to sit on one of the benches so I kept moving, trying to work out a logical course of action. But I felt powerless, dejected and angry. Logic did not come easily. There was no one to turn to for advice so I would simply have to keep stumbling along in ignorance. The tide of helplessness that had lapped against my emotions for months, washed over me unabated in great waves.

What had the GP written in my notes when I had walked out? Perhaps his view that everything was in my mind would affect the opinion of any future doctors I went to for help. Medical aid seemed to be more difficult to obtain as my health worsened.

A squirrel ran along the ground in front of me. There was little that could be achieved during the couple of weeks remaining before returning north for Christmas. The holiday would be used to plan a new course of action although, as the squirrel climbed a nearby tree, I had no idea of what this new path could possibly be.

The time was spent making sure essays and assignments were completely up-to-date. End of term parties were largely ignored. They had never appealed much. Watford College was dominated by male students so these events tended to be nothing more than heavy drinking sessions, normally without any female company. The college had been a great disappointment on that score.

The journey from Kings Cross to Newcastle was un-eventful and late one morning I was once more standing against the radiator in my parents' sitting room, drinking tea out of a cup and saucer from their Pyrex dinner service. This had been in the family for longer than me and it was totally indestructible. I had often mused on the idea that if a nuclear bomb dropped on Gateshead, the only things that would survive were Mam's Pyrex dinner service and the cock-roaches that appeared in our bathroom a little too frequently for my liking.

Mam was drinking her tea while sitting in the chair by the electric fire. The bars weren't on, so the wooden fire screen was in its usual place. The entire front of the screen was inlaid with matchsticks, skilfully cut and varnished to create intricate patterns. When I was young, picking up matchsticks in the street for Dad's stock had been an on-going activity. Any walk outside would include looking out for them. Over the years I must have collected thousands!

Dad was in the underground boiler house. Once a week a lorry delivered coal through a hatch in the ground and it would drop from here into a large hopper below. There were three blocks of flats, and when a caretaker was on duty one of his jobs was to shovel coal from the hopper into the boilers that burned constantly, producing hot water for washing and heating, like the water that was running through the radiator behind me.

Mam could see the weight loss, but made no comment and asked how I was getting on at college. I didn't mention visiting the Harley Street specialist, or tell her the latest opinion of the Watford GP. Instead, I explained how the holiday would be used to write letters seeking employment.

June might have been a long way off, but there would be a significant number of students with printing qualifications looking for work at the same time, and competition for good jobs would be fierce. Before leaving Watford I had borrowed a directory of UK print-related companies and would use my old Imperial typewriter to write as many letters as possible over the break.

Mam thought it a good idea and went off to finish dinner so I took the opportunity to play my piano, which had been bought for me when I was twelve. One of my few favourable memories of school is of the music teacher I had who insisted I should have an instrument of some sort.

We weren't a musical family so the concept was rather alien to us, but Mam persuaded Dad we should buy a piano and many weeks were spent checking the 'For Sale' items in the *Gateshead Post*. We eventually found something. It cost twenty-five pounds, a huge sum, and made up my Christmas and birthday presents for years afterwards. I always felt a bit guilty about how it rather dominated the room.

Christmas Day was quiet. It always was. The three of us celebrated with a chicken, the only time in the year we ate it as chicken was an expensive meat then. I was just glad I wasn't ill. We sat quietly around the kitchen table, the silence broken by the odd snippet of conversation. There was certainly no alcohol. Our bottle of sherry was only brought out for guests, so lasted years. Later, we would watch the Queen on television and then whatever film came on afterwards, which was invariably something we had seen.

As we ate, my mind wandered back to a Christmas four years earlier. Mam and Dad had been in the kitchen and unknown to them I had dressed in my kilt and black jacket then took my pipes out of their case. This was for Mam. She was so proud of me wearing the kilt and playing the pipes. They caught a flash of tartan passing the kitchen entrance, but I was out of the front door and down the steps before either of them could utter a word.

The block was constructed in an L-shape and when I stood outside the kitchen window I was between the two wings of the building. Mam and Dad moved the net curtain aside and watched with expressions of apprehension. I was about to stick my head above the parapet of obscurity, and we simply didn't *do* that sort of thing. I had deliberately waited until after twelve o'clock, so anyone sleeping off a late night would have less reason to complain.

I inflated the bag, tuned the pipes and began my first slow air. Within moments, heads were popping out of windows all over. Several people walked along the main corridor and opened one of the windows to watch with elbows resting on the sill. They listened all the way up to the seventh floor. Mam's earlier expression had been replaced by a small smile.

At the start of my second tune an elderly woman from a ground-floor flat headed towards me in her slippers and thick woollen cardigan. When she was still many yards away she stretched out a hand. Not for an instant during my planning had I considered this possibility, which filled me with as much dread as if she had been the Grim Reaper.

I tried to move away, but my hands were playing the chanter and I couldn't speak because of blowing down the mouthpiece. She followed me and we danced around each other, while our neighbours watched from every direction and my heart pounded with fear from what she was attempting to do.

In the end, there was no escape. The woman had known me as a small boy and I couldn't simply ignore her, couldn't leave her standing in her slippers and cardigan on a frosty winter's day, when all she meant was an act of kindness.

I stretched out my hand. As she dropped the coins into my palm it wasn't only the music that was destroyed. My gesture to Mam was reduced to dust.

They think I'm playing for money.

I stuffed the coins into my pocket and picked up the tune again, while the old woman walked stiffly back to the warmth of her electric fire. My pride crumbled into shame. I didn't have the courage to look up at the kitchen window. Cutting the tune short, I tucked the pipes under my arm and strode back into the main entrance as if marching. But in reality it was to get out of sight as quickly as possible. People clapped and cheered, but it didn't relieve the sting of bitter disappointment; not one tiny part of it.

I was brought back to the present by Mam asking me a question about the bread sauce. I smiled across the table and said it was good. She always made bread sauce to go with the chicken, which meant we ate it only once a year.

When the meal was over Mam and Dad washed up. There wasn't actually room in the kitchen for three people to try and clear up, so I went into the sitting room and ended up flicking through a *Yellow Pages* directory, which for some reason was lying out. (I said Christmas Day was quiet).

The pages stopped at the section for the letter 'I' and in curiosity I sought out the first reference, which turned out to be for 'ice cream manufacturer's equipment'. Then my eye was drawn to the wording above ... and suddenly I knew what my next step was going to be.

Chapter Twelve

By the end of the Christmas break I had posted around sixty letters to companies throughout the UK, asking if there might be a vacancy in the summer. I returned to Gammons Lane late on the Sunday afternoon, the day before college was due to resume. Once I had unpacked and said hello to Mr and Mrs Wilcox and Paul, I sat down with the local telephone directory, which was always on the cabinet by the front door.

It was obviously laid out in a similar manner to the one in Gateshead and sandwiched between 'hygiene and cleaning services' and 'ice cream manufacturer's equipment' was a reference to 'hypnotherapists', which was what had caught my eye while in my parents' sitting room.

What I was trying to do was use a specialist to disprove the GP's theory that the illness was being caused by my imagination. Perhaps I should have looked up 'psychiatrist', but apart from not being able to spell the word, such things were beyond my comprehension. At least I had some idea of what a hypnotist did. I had seen them on television.

This tactic was, of course, completely flawed, as proven so concisely by the osteopath who, instead of confirming there was nothing wrong with my spine, had found a hat-trick of bulging discs. That had been a close escape. But I was becoming more desperate, so I scanned down the list of possibilities. There were a surprising number of hypno-therapists listed and after about twenty minutes I had still not made a decision.

Should I go for a DPH, MSAPP or LNCP? There were as many different letters as names, and none of them meant a thing to me. Did a large advertisement imply they were successful and therefore good? Or, as I had no transport, should I pick someone who lived nearby? Some offered psychotherapy, while others included counselling. Perhaps I should just ring a few and see who sounded the friendliest? Also, although I was resigned to the likely event of going into debt to try and find a cure, the cost couldn't be ignored completely.

The physiotherapist in the dance class had been able to recommend a Harley Street specialist, but I didn't feel inclined to ask amongst friends if anyone knew a good hypnotherapist. I feared that while one might raise sympathy, the other might raise eyebrows. In the end, I went for someone who had as many letters as anyone else and who lived only a short bus ride away, with the proviso that if he sounded 'odd' I would try somebody else. The next day, after college, I rang.

'Hello,' said the voice.

It was a woman.

'I'd like to make an appointment, please,' I said.

'Certainly, I'll just get my husband.'

The line went quiet. Did this mean her husband was the hypnotherapist or he kept the diary? Moments later, a man's voice came over the telephone.

'Hello. Can I help you?'

He sounded fairly normal so I arranged an appointment for one Wednesday afternoon, at the beginning of February. I had begun my quest once more, but my reserves were being stretched.

Replies to my job application letters began to arrive within days of returning to Watford, and included within the many 'No thank you' answers was one that caught my attention immediately. It was from a Mr R. Coxhead, editor of the weekly trade magazine *Printing World*. He was coming to Watford College at the end of January to attend the annual award ceremony, and suggested we meet up during the evening.

The letter was a cause of great excitement because, of all the potential careers in print I could pursue, this was the one I wanted most. It would give me the opportunity to write. I telephoned the magazine and confirmed with the secretary that I would be at the event. The secretary, Phyll, told me she would also be attending, along with the editor's wife, and said if I carried a copy of *Printing World*, they would all look out for me.

The awards were for students who had left college the previous year and the evening was not usually open to those still attending, so I had to call on the help of my course tutor to obtain an invitation. My only concern was that I wouldn't be well enough to make it. I had been lucky over Christmas and escaped lightly while in Gateshead.

Mam and Dad hadn't realised how my health was deteriorating. However, since coming back, the sickness and pain had returned with a severity and frequency greater than ever. The attacks came at any time and I could wake in the morning feeling fine, but be forced back to bed by lunchtime.

Apart from college work, my main focus became what I would say to the editor. By the time the day arrived, I could recite my 'speech' fluently. When the last class finished that Friday afternoon I hurried back to Gammons Lane to polish shoes, wash and get ready to return to the college.

There wasn't a lot of choice in terms of what to wear so I

put on my smartest pair of trousers, shirt and tie, then my jacket, which failed to match anything, but was all I had. When I studied the result in the full length mirror on the inside of the wardrobe door, my heart sank.

I had stopped weighing myself when the pointer on the bathroom scales had dropped below eight and a half stones. I didn't know what my weight was now, but 'gaunt' was hardly an accurate description for my six foot one inch frame.

Moving to the other side of the room I walked back towards the mirror, holding out my hand and smiling as if meeting the editor. It wasn't impressive. There was little I could do about the sunken cheeks and pasty complexion, but if I could find a way of not appearing so thin ... I took off the jacket, found the thickest jumper in the chest-of-drawers and put both items on. It looked faintly ridiculous. However, I could think of nothing else. Time was running short, so I put on my overcoat, picked up the copy of *Printing World* I had borrowed earlier from the library and set off.

As I walked briskly along the road I went through my 'speech' again and, all things considered, thought it was pretty impressive. I actually had no idea what qualifications or experience the editor might require for a reporter, but I had spent four years in the printing industry and would hopefully have an HND in Printing by the summer.

Also, I had always wanted to write, liked meeting people, would be willing to travel for the job and was happy to move to Kent, which was where the publishing house was based. I had practised answers to every question I could think of that he might possibly ask me. All that was needed was the opportunity to present my case. It seemed to have fallen neatly into my lap.

Arriving shortly after seven o'clock I deposited my coat at the cloakroom and joined the slow-moving queue making its way into the hall, which was filling up with a mixture of lecturers, parents, people from the industry and ex-students.

The two front rows on either side of the aisle were empty and these were being kept free for that evening's dignitaries, who had been invited for a pre-ceremony drink with the senior lecturers and, at that very moment, would be in the principal's office, scoffing the college's sherry. By seven-thirty the hall was packed and one of the lecturers walked on to the stage and asked us to stand. I had never been to an event like this before, so everything about it was new.

We stood and a few moments later the principal, followed by other senior members of staff, walked down the aisle and on to the stage. They were followed by the evening's special guests, who were mainly leading figures in the printing industry, several of them representing major manufacturers that had sponsored awards. They sat in the two front rows and we were told to sit. It was already getting uncomfortably warm and I was beginning to wonder at the wisdom of my choice of clothes.

The principal gave a talk about the level of technology utilised in a modern printing industry and the need for highly-trained students to operate equipment and to be future leaders. He stressed, no doubt partly for the benefit of attending company managing directors, the need for manufacturers to support educational establishments, and offered a grateful thanks to those that had recently donated machinery and money. He then introduced the guest speaker, who was presenting the prizes and we got down to the real business of the evening.

Line after line of ex-students walked across the stage until it seemed that almost everyone in the hall was going to be given something: City & Guilds; diplomas; higher diplomas; degrees. Those receiving the awards were dressed in everything from jeans to suits with cap and gown and after many handshakes and bursts of applause it was the turn of those who had won special prizes to go back on stage. These were the best of the previous year's final students.

I sat forward in my seat when the person walked on stage to accept the award for Best Student on the HND in Printing course. I knew the lad as he had started with me, but whereas I had gone into industry he had continued, so my year out had been his final one.

As he shook hands with the guest speaker my mind drifted away from the crowded hall, back to the reason that I had ended up working in print; an industry my family had no connections with. In many ways the journey had begun when I was ten; the year in which Gateshead Council abolished the grammar school system within the areas under their control. They were one of the first (if not *the* first) councils in England to do so. Granted, I might not have consumed sufficient fish fingers to have passed the Eleven Plus, but it would have been nice to have been given the opportunity.

Instead, I disappeared into an education system where a large proportion of those involved were completely against learning, either for themselves or allowing others to learn, while a lad who played the piano was one to be vilified. I had buckled under years of verbal abuse and, later, failed dismally at my A Levels, when I could have done better. There was no question of going to university or college and I was sick to death of the whole system anyway. It was a miserable period.

My only option had been to start scanning the 'jobs vacant' section of the *Gateshead Post*, and only weeks after leaving school there had been an advertisement for a trainee estimator/production controller at the printing company that I looked at every time I opened the bedroom curtains. It was having worked in the industry for three years that had provided me with the necessary entry 'qualification' to go to college.

I was brought back to the present by laughter in the hall. Someone had made a funny comment, but I had missed it. I continued to think about that prize. It wasn't enough for me to get the HND. I wanted the prize for Best Student.

This aim wasn't based on any illusions about my abilities. There were plenty of much brighter people than me on the course, plus several who had completed apprenticeships, so they knew certain aspects of the industry better than I ever would. A few others had fathers who owned, or were managing directors, of printing companies, so had a history in it, and were being groomed for influential posts of the future. But I believed I had one advantage over them all. I had something to prove.

The ceremony drew to a close with a round-up of thanks from the principal, who then led his guests out of the hall and towards the canteen and waiting buffet. The rest of us, having been asked to stand, were once more told to sit. We were entertained to a series of jokes and anecdotes from a Welsh lecturer who was renowned for telling funny stories. When he had judged that the special guests had been served with their wine and vol-au-vents, he instructed us to make our way to the canteen.

I was glad to stand as it had been getting increasingly hot in the hall. Unfortunately, the canteen was not designed for so many people and quickly became even worse. I fought my way to the bar, where two of the kitchen staff were frantically serving drinks, and grabbed an orange juice. Then I forced my way through the crowds until I was roughly in the centre of the room. I held the copy of *Printing World* against my chest, but unless someone was standing next to me it was impossible to see. Finding the editor was going to be much more difficult than I had imagined.

More than once someone looked intently at the magazine and then at me, but when I smiled they always turned away. This was not going well. Making circuits of the room, I swapped my empty glass for another orange juice at every opportunity. After half an hour of grinning manically at complete strangers only to be ignored, I was beginning to develop a complex when someone tapped me on the shoulder.

'Hello,' said the blond woman with the tapping hand. 'I'm Phyll, Roy's secretary. We saw you wandering around, but you kept disappearing.'

'Oh, hello. Where are you?'

'We've got a table to ourselves in the corner.'

I followed Phyll, straightening my tie, which I had loosened and quickly wiping my brow with a hanky as we went. She took me to a table at which were sitting a bald-headed chap in his early fifties and a dark-haired woman, whom I took to be the editor and his wife. The man stood up.

'Ah, you must be Philip. I'm Roy and this is my wife Pat,' he said.

'I'm very pleased to meet you,' I said, shaking the offered hands.

Was my Geordie accent too strong?

We sat around the table and exchanged a few pleasantries

about the awards and our relative journeys to Watford. At the first pause, without, I hoped, it being too abrupt, I launched into my well-researched dialogue.

'Well, I've always been interested in going into journa …'

'Roy! How are you?' said a voice, booming out from somewhere behind me.

'Hello,' said the editor, standing up.

I stood as well, thinking it the polite thing to do. The owner of the voice fought his way through the crowds.

'How are you Roy? I've not seen you in ages. You've met my wife I believe …'

The crowd closed around them like a Venus flytrap with an insect, and they were gone. I looked in bewilderment at the two women who had remained sitting at the table.

'I'm sorry,' said Pat.

'It's always the same,' said Phyll.

'Oh,' I answered, sitting down hesitantly. 'Very popular I suppose.'

'Yes,' they replied together.

'If someone doesn't drag him away, he's always dashing off with a notebook in his hand because he's seen someone he wants to interview,' said Phyll.

'All part of being an editor,' I ventured.

The two women nodded in agreement. I was rather at a loss and there was a slight pause in the conversation.

'Don't mind me saying, but aren't you rather hot with that jumper and jacket on?' enquired the secretary. 'You do look a little … flushed.'

'Hot? Goodness no. Ha ha. No. I always have a good ruddy complexion,' I said, sweat running down my back.

We sat making small talk for some time until eventually we got around to me and the job on *Printing World*. It seemed like a good chance to practise my speech so I began to go through all the points that I felt would put me in a good light. We had been talking for quite some while when Roy returned.

'Hello again,' he said emerging from the crowd. 'Sorry about that, but it was someone I hadn't seen in a long time.'

'Any stories?' asked Pat.

'A few,' he replied, patting his pocket, which I took to be where he kept his notebook. He turned to me.

'Now, Philip, tell me about yourself.'

This was my chance. I really wanted this job.

'Well, I've always been interested in going ...'

'Look!' said Phyll. 'There's Michael. You wanted to catch him.'

Roy followed his secretary's gaze.

'Yes. Yes, I do.'

His hand was already reaching inside his pocket as he stood.

'I'll just grab him while he's near. Excuse me, Philip. I won't be a minute.'

'Of course. No problem,' I said, standing as he left then sitting down again.

I thought I was about to explode with the heat and offered to fetch drinks from the bar. I returned about ten minutes later and sat down once more with the two women.

'So, tell us a little more about what you have been doing at college,' said Phyll.

I covered my course work, what I had been doing during my time in industry and the special projects I had completed. The more I told them the more they questioned, until they both said together.

'There's Roy.'

I looked around and started to rise. Roy was making his way back to the table, less hindered now as people were beginning to leave. When he was about four yards away a hand shot out from a group of men he was passing and clasped him on the shoulder. I couldn't believe it. He was gone again. I sat down.

The night wore on. More people left and it reached the point where there weren't many remaining. Roy had disappeared completely from view. At the table we had long since exhausted our conversation about the job. The two women kept looking at their watches. It was nearly eleven o'clock and they had yet to travel back to Tonbridge.

'Ah, here you still are,' said Roy, who had appeared without me seeing him approach. 'Well, I suppose we'd better be moving. Sorry we haven't had longer to chat, Philip. Give me a ring in a few weeks and we'll fix something up.'

I muttered several comments along the lines of, 'Think nothing of it', and 'It's been a very pleasant evening'. We walked together to the cloakroom and had just collected our coats when someone collared Roy again. It was time to go. I said farewell to Pat and Phyll and, feeling extremely deflated, made my way glumly back to Gammons Lane.

Chapter Thirteen

I had told no one about my appointment with the hypnotherapist and the burden of the secret added to the apprehension I was already feeling over the approaching visit. I couldn't help wondering what he would be like. Did he have 'staring eyes' or a pocket watch, which he would swing to and fro in front of me? I knew nothing about him other than his advertisement in *Yellow Pages*.

The hypnotherapist worked from home and I discovered after getting off the bus that this was in a very well-to-do area. When I was standing outside his front door, I put away the scrap of paper containing his address and rang the bell. It was several moments before I saw a shape on the other side of the frosted glass. He was a bit of a disappointment. Not a pocket watch in sight and a normal pair of eyes. In fact, he looked like a normal middle-aged bloke.

'Mr Paris? Please come in,' he said.

Even his voice didn't sound unusual. Apparently, I was a little early and he still had the previous patient upstairs. He asked me to wait on a chair, then walked quickly back up the stairs and through a half-open door at the top, which he closed quietly behind him.

Though I tried not to take any notice, it was impossible not to hear his voice and he appeared to be bringing someone back to the world of consciousness. There was silence for a short while then the door opened and a smart-looking woman of about thirty-five came down the stairs, followed by the hypnotherapist. As she reached the last few steps I wasn't sure whether to acknowledge her or not and in the end decided to pretend I wasn't there, which was just as well because she also made out I was invisible. Moments later, I entered the room that had just been vacated.

'Why don't you take off your jacket and shoes and lie on the couch,' he said.

I did as instructed and he sat down at the other side of his desk. The hypnotherapist turned out to be one of those people who feel the best way to make you at ease is to tell you about their problems, so for the first ten minutes I heard about his marital troubles. I offered what were, hopefully, suitable comments at appropriate moments.

Eventually, we got around to why I was there and how he could help me. I took a deep breath and told him about my illness, beginning with how I had woken one day with a dull ache. The hypnotherapist at least had a sense of humour, because he laughed loudly at how the white medicine had given me the 'squits'. I finished my story by explaining about the latest diagnosis and the 'treatment' with Valium.

'Dear, dear. What a trial,' he said, leaning back in his chair. 'What an unnecessary amount of suffering when all along this has clearly been caused by tension. It's such a very common thing for tension to manifest itself as pain in the lower back. I've treated this exact condition so many times. It's a pity you didn't see someone like me earlier on.'

As he said these last words, music began to play, although, at first, it was so quiet I wasn't certain if I had imagined it.

'Why don't you close your eyes for a while and make yourself comfortable. I'm sure I can help you. Clear your mind of all those everyday thoughts. It's a problem that can be cured in just a few visits.' He paused. 'I want you to imagine you are going down in a lift ... down into your subconscious, and as the lift passes each level, so you become more relaxed and at peace. Relaxed and at peace.

'If any other thoughts come into your mind, just push them gently away. Relax. Go down into your subconscious. Deeper. As the lift reaches the bottom so you become totally relaxed and all your worries and anxieties fade away.'

He was now speaking in a flat monotone voice. The music continued.

'When the lift stops, the door opens, and you find yourself in a garden. Step out into the garden. It's a warm sunny day and the grass beneath your feet is soft and cool. Walk through the garden, for it's your garden; there's no one else and so no need to be concerned.

'As you walk you find that your right hand is getting lighter. In fact, it begins to feel so weightless that you want to lift it into the air.'

To my utter surprise, it did feel lighter and when he said the words to me again I raised my hand a few inches off the couch.

'And now your arm feels heavier once more and you want to rest it.'

I laid it down.

'You're lying on the grass and the hot sun is warming your body. As it does all the tension, particularly that in your lower back, is fading away. As the muscles slacken you know you will never feel pain in your back again because the reason has gone ... Enjoy lying in the sun and relax ... reeelaaax ...'

He stopped speaking and I lay, listening to the gently soothing music for quite some time. I can only guess the hypnotherapist was sitting behind his desk watching. Or maybe he was reading the newspaper. I don't know how long I was there before he spoke again.

'It's time to get off the grass and return to the conscious world. But even when you leave the garden you will be relaxed. Get up and walk into the lift, start to climb up from your subconscious. The lift is getting higher and you'll soon be properly awake. When you are, all the pain and tension will have gone and it won't return.

'The lift is at level five now and when it reaches number ten you'll wake up and feel well. You'll feel confident and happy and relaxed. Six … seven … eight … nine … ten. Wake up now … you're wide awake.'

I opened my eyes and looked across at the hypnotherapist, who was sitting behind his desk, just as he had been when I first lay on the couch. The music had stopped, although I hadn't been aware of it being turned off.

'How do you feel?'

His voice had resumed the normal inflections of everyday speech.

'Well, thank you.'

Indeed, I did feel okay; just the same as when I had arrived.

'That's very good. It won't take long to eliminate this pain. I think I should see you for five or six more visits. We can talk about anything that might make you feel tense or worried, then we'll go through a tension release exercise, which will rid you once and for all of any tightness in your muscles.'

'Right,' I said, nodding my head.

Not really sure what else to say I put on my shoes, glancing at my watch as I bent down. I had been there nearly an hour. It hadn't seemed that long. When I had fastened my laces and we agreed a date in ten days' time for my return, there was only one thing left unanswered.

'Who do I make the cheque payable to?'

The hypnotherapist might have been surprised to see me the next morning with my head hanging over the toilet, but I wasn't. Most of the afternoon was spent in bed. The attacks had fallen into roughly a six-day cycle.

The post normally included a letter or two in reply to my mass mailing over the Christmas holiday, and on the Friday of that week an envelope arrived from a printing company in Leeds called John Blackburn. They were big. I had heard of the name even before coming across them in the directory of printing companies. One of the managers was interested in meeting and asked if I would make an appointment.

I rang that day and, trying to estimate when I was least likely to be ill, made an appointment for the following Friday. As I had calculated, I was sick at the beginning of the week but okay by the end. It was a grey, bleak morning when I left Watford to make my way to Kings Cross, and when I arrived in Leeds it had also proved to be a grey, bleak journey. I'm not really into omens or this might have alerted me to the events that were about to take place.

The manager told me that the factory was within walking distance of the railway station, so I set off, following the directions he had provided. I don't know what his idea of walking distance was, but it was a long time before the building came into sight. The walk hadn't put me in a very good frame of mind for an interview.

He met me in reception and we went to his office where he took my coat and arranged for coffee. It's difficult to put a finger on what was wrong. My experience and qualifications seemed to be exactly what he wanted and the timing of my departure from college fitted in perfectly with his requirements. However, we both knew early on that the job and I were not for each other. We went through the motions. He asked his questions and gave me the opportunity to ask mine.

It was all over quite quickly and I felt pretty disappointed by how the day was turning out. He did redeem himself at the end of the meeting when he asked how much it had cost me to get there. I added up my train and underground tickets and when I told him the figure he handed over the amount in cash without question, which impressed me greatly. It had cost a small fortune attending interviews at printing colleges around the country when I had been looking for a place.

'I'll show you around the factory if you like,' he said.

It's always interesting to walk around printing plants and having travelled all that way it would have been a shame not to have a tour. But we had no sooner left his office when he suddenly raced ahead of me at such a great speed I had to almost run to catch up, even with my long legs. It struck me that perhaps he had been taking some of the same white medicine I had been given. When I caught up he said,

'People who work for me have to be able to keep up with me in everything I do. I always find that if they can't match me while I'm walking, they won't in anything else.'

In this ridiculous manner, I jogged around the entire factory, which was not small, and was out on the pavement again soon afterwards. I was glad to be alone. The rain had started to fall heavily, but I had asked the receptionist if she could tell me how to find the stop to catch a bus to the main railway station. As I entered the meagre shelter the rain was pelting down, which did nothing for my flagging spirits.

The only person there was a woman in her early twenties who stared at me. There was a train to Kings Cross in about thirty minutes. The one after that was an hour later. If a bus came soon, the first one would be a possibility. The minutes ticked by, the rain beat down and the woman glowered. We were total strangers. What on earth could I have possibly done to offend her?

Salvation came in sight when a taxi came along. Blow the cost. I really didn't fancy hanging around Leeds station, so I dashed out of the shelter and waved frantically. The afternoon was turning black and visibility was poor. The car stopped a few yards further on so I ran after it and was so pleased that I got in next to the driver.

'What dreadful weather,' I said, dripping water over everything in sight. 'I'm certainly glad you came along when you did. Could you take me to the station please?'

It was only as I had said this and was putting on my seat belt that I looked over at the driver. The man, fear etched clearly upon his face, had undone his seat belt and was edging towards his door, which he had opened several inches.

'No,' he stammered.

'No?' I replied, astonished at such a straightforward request.

'No,' said the man again, opening his door wider and moving even nearer to it.

'But ... why not?

'I'm not a taxi,' said the man, one leg almost completely out of the door.

As the realisation of what he said dawned upon me, a little cry of despair escaped from somewhere deep within. I glanced at his windscreen and could see the sticker that ran along the top didn't say the magic word 'Taxi', which I had thought it did only moments earlier.

A second, louder moan escaped at the acknowledgement that another of life's great embarrassing moments was about to descend upon me.

'You're ... not a taxi?'

I spoke with as much amazement as I could muster, and almost added 'are you certain?' But even as the words were leaving my lips I knew in my heart the situation was hopeless.

With many apologies, my hopes that his leg would soon dry and my best wishes for a speedy journey wherever he was going, I climbed out into the storm and headed back to the bus stop. The woman was absolutely beside herself, huffing and muttering, as if my mistake had been a personal insult to every ancestor she ever had.

The car drove off and a few moments later a bus arrived. The woman sat near the front so I went towards the back, but if I thought that her onslaught was over I was mistaken for she had sat next to someone she knew.

The bus had only just pulled away when they both turned around and the first woman pointed directly at me. The pair must have attended special evening classes in scowling because they were bloody experts at it.

And what happened next? Oh great. At the next stop two women got on who knew the first one, and the bus hadn't even moved when all four turned around and the first woman pointed again for the benefit of her newly arrived friends. They had all taken the same course in humanity and communication.

I was so fed up. Cold, wet and hungry, the entire day had

been a total waste of time and there were still several hours of travelling yet to do. All the way to the station the four women would turn around periodically to glower at me, as if they somehow expected my appearance to have changed from only a few minutes earlier when they had last looked.

Chapter Fourteen

One of the regular local barn dances was held the following night and when, during the interval, I recounted the tale of the previous day's journey, Babs almost fell off her chair laughing.

'They're a hard lot in Leeds,' she said, wiping away tears.

These evenings were a lifeline. The local Scottish country dance classes and events were more difficult for me to get to, so my time was mainly confined to English folk dancing, although I did have my kilt with me and donned it on a few occasions. That night ended as they always did, at someone's house for tea, biscuits and conversation. Dancing provided the balance to my life.

Since the disastrous night at the college awards ceremony, I had been wondering what to do about contacting the editor of *Printing World*, and decided I should offer to go to the offices in Tonbridge for a proper interview. During the Monday morning break, when other students went to the canteen, I made my way to the telephone booths situated at the main entrance and dialled the number. A few moments later the secretary put me through to the editor.

'Good morning, Mr Coxhead. I thought I should give you a ring about the interview,' I said in my best accent, ready to add that I could travel to Kent whenever suited him.

'Oh, yes, yes. Well, just let my secretary know exactly when you want to start,' he replied. 'I believe you're leaving college in June, so why don't we say August?'

I must have misheard.

'Sorry ... did you say you wanted me to begin in August?'

'Didn't I send you a letter? Oh, I'm sorry. I'll get one off tomorrow. Yes. It all seems in order to me. Just sort out a date with Phyll, and I look forward to seeing you in a few months' time.'

'Right. Certainly. Well, thanks very much. Marvellous,' I said in such rapid succession that the words were all jumbled together. My heart was pounding.

'Good luck with the finals. Goodbye.'

'Oh, yes. Goodbye,' I said.

The line had gone dead. It took a long time to compose myself after I put down the receiver, because there was a shout of joy building up inside me that would have been heard throughout the college had I let it out.

The letter arrived a few days later, confirming that my first day as a trainee reporter on *Printing World* would be 8th August, 1983. In addition, I was to be enrolled in the company's two-year journalist training scheme, which covered an extensive range of subjects, from shorthand to copyright law. I danced around the room at Gammons Lane like someone, as we might say in Gateshead 'Away with the mixer'. Paul was completely bemused by my behaviour, which he attributed to eating too much haggis.

Having a job lined up, and the very one I wanted, lifted a great weight from my mind. Now the focus was on getting better and passing my finals. Despite swimming several times a week and seeing the hypnotherapist, the attacks fell into a five-day cycle, just as I feared they would. My last appointment with the hypnotherapist was booked for the end of March. He had mentioned several times that during this session we would go through a final, tension-release exercise, though I had no idea what this entailed.

The other sessions had been similar to the first, with a trip down the lift and a walk past the roses. Entering his room, the treatment became different as soon as I had taken off my shoes. Rather than using the couch, he told me to lie on the floor.

'I want you to make yourself completely comfortable,' he said. 'If you've got any itches, please scratch them (this was a much-used little joke). Just lie there for a moment, clear your mind of all thoughts except what I am going to tell you. Today, we're going to get rid of the last of the tension in your body and with that you will never again feel pain in your back.'

I had mentioned to him during earlier visits that the severity and frequency of the attacks were increasing, but this seemed only to convince him further that the 'tension-release' exercise was the treatment needed. I closed my eyes and music once again filtered gently throughout the room. The speakers must have been cleverly hidden because I had never spotted them.

'You're going down in the lift now. You know there's nothing to worry about because you've done it so many times. In fact, you look forward to walking through the garden. Go down now, deeper into your subconscious.'

His voice had taken on the flat, monotone sound I had come to know so well.

'As the lift goes down from level five … to four … you're slipping deeper into your subconscious. Deeeeper. Three … two … one.'

He stopped speaking and I could hear nothing for several moments apart from the music.

'But I don't want you to relax. I want you to feel tension spreading up your body, starting with your toes. Tense those toes and then your feet. Let me see them stretching down.'

The monotone voice had gone and the hypnotherapist was ordering me like an angry headmaster with a pupil.

'I want that tension to spread up into your calves. Tighten those muscles. Feel them go hard, as it moves up into your thighs. From your toes to your thighs are now so taut that they're rigid. Hold that sensation. Concentrate on it.'

He paused for a moment. I was aware of my legs having lifted off the floor and waving slightly in the air.

'Now it's moving up into your body. And all the muscles in your stomach are becoming tight and those in your sides and those in your back; tighter and tighter, until they're like rocks. And still your legs are taut.'

The faceless voice became louder and more commanding until it sounded like a sergeant shouting at a private on the parade ground.

'It's up into your chest and shoulders. You can feel them stiffen. And now the tension is travelling down your arms and all the muscles in your upper arms and then your lower arms are becoming tight, right down to your fingertips. Stretch those arms and hands as it travels up into your neck and head, until it's in your cheeks, even those in your brow.'

He stopped. I felt, as I always did when 'put under' that I could get up and walk away at any time, and whether this was how you were supposed to feel when hypnotised, I didn't know. But because he was trying to help I wanted to do what he told me. Perhaps this was also an essential part of the process.

I lay on the floor, a mass of quivering arms and legs as the tension in my body increased until it felt as though I would snap, like something that's become so frozen and brittle the merest touch could cause it to shatter. Everything was aching. Even my teeth were so tightly clenched I thought they were in danger of being ground into stumps.

In the part of me that wasn't so rigid it didn't work anymore, I felt there was something unwholesome about it all; lying on the floor of a house, while someone who was virtually a stranger commanded me to do bizarre things. This was not a pleasant walk through the garden.

I was back on the wrong train and this time it was careering out of control … in a long dark tunnel … no hope of escape … no way of avoiding the impending collision. But I had boarded the train willingly, looked up its departure time and platform in a directory between 'hygiene and cleaning services' and 'ice cream manufacturer's equipment'. There was no one else to blame for this journey except myself.

What had I done?

An age seemed to pass as I lay there, shaking in the blackness of the tunnel, travelling ever faster towards a dead end. My mind screamed out for him to stop it.

'Now relax,' he commanded. 'Let that tension out of your body. Relax those muscles ... all of them ... in your head and shoulders, down your arms and into your hands. Let the muscles in your chest and stomach go slack, and those in your legs go loose.'

I expelled my breath in a great sigh, my whole body going limp like a rag doll.

'Relax. You're lying in the garden and the sun is on your body. You'll never feel that tension again. It's all gone. You have seen it go, particularly that in your lower back.'

His voice had taken on that of the familiar, soothing friend.

'Just relax.'

I was aware of the music again, the same soft music that had accompanied me on so many botanical missions.

'Relax.'

I lost track of time.

'You're getting up and leaving the garden now. Climb into the lift that's waiting for you and come back to the conscious world. When you step out and leave this room ... and this house ... you will never feel any pain in your lower back. The lift is going up. When it reaches level number ten you'll wake up, and you'll feel well and content and happy. Six ... seven ... eight ... nine ... ten.'

I opened my eyes to see the hypnotherapist leaning against his desk.

'How are you?' he asked as if we were two old acquaintances meeting in the street.

'Fine,' I said.

But I wasn't really. I wanted away from the place. Standing up slowly I went over to sit on the couch to put on my shoes. He sat behind his desk.

'Well, I know you won't get any more trouble. You'll find that now the tension has all gone, these recurring attacks have disappeared.'

He talked on as I fastened my laces. He was so confident. I suppose being positive was vital. If he planted a seed of doubt in a patient's mind it could grow into something that might undo a lot of what had been achieved. I had gone to him with an entire garden of doubts and nothing he had done during the previous two months had made them wilt in the slightest. I wrote out a cheque and left.

Chapter Fifteen

The Easter break was spent in Gateshead. I tried to play down the recent attacks and certainly didn't mention my visits to the hypnotherapist, but as Mam and I chatted in the kitchen there was no hiding the fact that things were not right. We both agreed how mysterious the illness was. Mam and Dad were delighted about the job on *Printing World* though they had hoped I would have found something a little closer to the North-East than Kent.

It was a Monday morning, which meant it was wash day. Every activity had its allotted place in the week. Baths were taken on a Friday, although I was always a bit fastidious about cleanliness and had an extra bath on a Tuesday. I was a strange lad at times.

We didn't have a washing machine, only an old circular electric boiler, which lived between the cooker and the sink. Mam would pull this out every week and set it up. The boiler didn't agitate the water so she did this with a poss-stick, which she would thrust into the water, up and down, round and round, up and down. The wood was white from years of being plunged into hot soapy water. I set up our old mangle on the kitchen table, so the washed sheets could later be fed through. It was extraordinary how dry they were after being squeezed by the rollers.

The Easter week passed quickly and I was ill for part of it. No one really knew what to suggest or do. By the Saturday, I was fine and that morning Mam and I stood at the kitchen window, watching a bride and groom with their guests outside the church opposite, on the other side of the toilets to the working men's club. I don't know if anyone ever left a morning service and went straight into the club to watch the strippers, who performed Sunday lunchtimes, but it was pretty handy for them if they did.

The local kids had gathered around the wedding car waiting outside the church. This always happened, because North-East wedding customs included a 'hoy-oot' where the bridegroom threw handfuls of coins out of the car as it drove away. This inevitably resulted in an incredible scramble, with fights often ensuing amongst the lads.

Mam and Dad would never dream of letting us boys demean ourselves, or risk getting hurt, at such an event, so we could only ever watch other children win the spoils of these occasions. We were a bit like that; watching life go by through the window, yet too horrified by the coarseness of it all to become involved.

My two brothers and their wives arrived after dinner, and later in the afternoon we gathered around to scream at the television because the wrestling was on. We loved them all: Big Daddy, Giant Haystacks, Jackie Pallo, Les Kellett, the Royal brothers. Shouting abuse at the television had been a regular event on a Saturday afternoon for as long as I could remember. I said farewell to my brothers and their families when they left, and the next day goodbye to my parents at Newcastle station. It was a sad journey back to Kings Cross.

A few days after returning to Watford I had one of the worst attacks yet. I felt pretty rough the following day and then was okay for two days, before having another severe attack on the Sunday. Now it was a four-day cycle.

Late morning on the following Thursday I was still lying in bed, but knew I would soon have to get up and make my way to the bathroom. I had already been violently sick several times since waking up. It felt as though I was being washed in pain, which swept up from low down on the right-hand side of my back and deep into my body. There was a bottle of painkillers on the locker next to the bed, but it was pointless to try and take any.

How I wished to be back in the bedroom of my childhood, so many hundreds of miles away, so many years earlier, when you knew you would be better when the demigod came; even if he didn't give you anything, because this meant your illness couldn't be that bad. You had trust and hope.

I looked at the bottle again. How many painkillers had been swallowed over the previous months? What damage had they done? Sometimes I would try to last out for as long as possible … just another hour … another ten minutes. On other occasions I would give in at the first sign of pain, with no thought of holding on.

I swore. It was no good. I would have to get up. Throwing the bedclothes off I sat up, swung my legs over the side of the bed and jumped down on to the floor. I had long since given up bothering to put on trousers or a dressing gown for these trips. Often there wasn't time and I didn't think old Mrs Wilcox, should she be around, was going to be bothered at the sight of my weedy body in a pair of underpants.

Locking the bathroom door I walked over to the toilet. I hated this. With great gasps that were not far from being sobs, I vomited until it seemed to me I must surely be no more than merely the shell of a figure; the outline of a man, but with nothing left inside.

I stayed with my hands on my knees, stooping over the porcelain, long after I had pressed the handle. The room spun as if my head was at the centre of a merry-go-round and all the animals raced faster and faster around me. In the end I was shaking with cold and exertion and knew I had to force myself to get back to bed. As I turned around I suddenly felt faint and, in fear of hurting myself in a fall, sank to my knees, collapsing over the side of the hard, enamelled bath.

Chapter Sixteen

I remained perfectly still, leaning with my arms on the side of the bath for a long, long time, head down by my hands, staring transfixed at the tiny droplets of water that were almost invisible against the whiteness below. Gradually, the dizziness and shaking subsided and my breathing became calm.

Without raising my head I turned it slowly to one side, a gesture of beginning to stand rather than actually thinking of doing it. As I did so, I looked into the face of a stranger ... a face that was both frightening and frightened. I didn't have the energy to be shocked; not the physical, jumping-back type of shock you get when you touched something too hot, but in my chest my heart had stopped. Was this really me?

I stared into the mirror with a sort of morbid fascination. It was as if my body was collapsing in upon itself; the skeleton trying to escape the skin that encased it. My bones protruded grotesquely: ribs, collar bones, those in my arms and legs, my hips.

But the worst things were the eyes: dead eyes; lifeless brown pools, like the water that collected in disused quarries, where nothing ever grew, where there were never any birds, and even on the sunniest, hottest day there was a coldness that chilled the bone, and an inexplicable loathing to hang around. I wanted to run back to the bedroom and bury myself in bed; to pretend that I hadn't seen.

I tried to work out why the eyes looked dead, because they couldn't be. I was there, kneeling by Mr Wilcox's bath with its big old brass taps that were difficult to turn. And then I realised ... there was no humour. The sparkle had gone and in the whole world there was nothing that would make them shine. No uncooked haggis being attacked on Burns night, not even Joe with his jokes about camels could bring back the sparkle. That was the worst.

For an instant, as I studied those empty, glazed eyes in their blackened sockets, I was reminded of Alfred. Tears rolled gently down my cheeks, falling silently on to the cold enamel below, then the image became a blur and I couldn't see anything.

I buried my head in my hands and stayed that way until the tears stopped, which was not for some time. But when I looked in the mirror again it was my own unshaven face I saw; pale and drawn, with the uncombed hair hanging tangled over the brow. Not a handsome face, even when well, but it was *mine*. And the eyes weren't dead, not by a long way yet, just tired.

Standing up, I spent several minutes at the sink, washing and rinsing the foul taste from my mouth then rubbed my cheeks hard with a towel until all traces of tears had gone. I would roll the dice again. The weeks spent with the hypno-therapist had been a wasteful diversion that I should not have allowed myself to follow. I would go back to the GP who had wanted to give me Valium, and insist he send me for more tests. It was all a matter of determination and I was determined ... I didn't have any time left not to be.

Psychiatrist or surgeon? The decision hung so finely in the balance that I dared not breathe for fear the movement of air would tip the scales against me. We had been sitting in silence for ages, yet still the GP said nothing. Instead, he tapped his pencil on the desk between us; first the rubber end, then sliding his fingers down the wood and swinging it around to put down the point. Rubber ... point ... *tap* ... *tap* ... psychiatrist ... surgeon ...

If he was shocked in any way at my appearance he kept it to himself. Having explained everything that had happened since our last meeting, I finished by telling him that the pain was not caused by my imagination. There must surely be tests that would be logical to send me for. For him to agree would be to admit that Valium was wrong, so we sat without speaking. Psychiatrist ... surgeon ... *tap* ... *tap* ... *tap* ...

'Have you ever had an IVP?'

He didn't explain what an IVP was. The name was unfamiliar so I shook my head. He had obviously decided the test would be a sensible step, yet he appeared unable to decide whether to organise this or not.

'I don't think an IVP will show anything, but if you really insist that I arrange it, I will.'

I nodded my head in reply, wanting only to get away and back to bed.

'Alright. I'll sort it out. The hospital will be in touch.'

Everyone at college was preparing frantically for their finals and we all tried to improve what remained of our course work, in order to offset any disasters in the exams. We also had to complete our third-year projects, which were to be handed in by the end of the term.

Mine was on the production of telephone directories in the UK, and I would have been hard pushed to have conjured up a less inspiring subject. However, I was able to call on my experience at the HSMO factory and Ben Johnson in York, because the latter also printed telephone directories. Despite everything, I threw myself into work and was still a contender for the title of Best Student.

A little over a week after my visit to the GP I received a letter from the hospital, giving me a date in the third week of April to attend for the IVP. I still hadn't found out what this test was, but arranged to be excused from classes yet again.

The hospital was only a walk of a few minutes from the college and I made my way to the X-ray department, as instructed in the letter. My fear of hospitals had vanished during this journey of mine to find a cure. When I had swapped my clothes for a gown, a nurse took me to the radiographer who asked me to lie on a table, which was positioned underneath a large metal contraption. She stood next to me.

'This is not like a conventional X-ray, which shows up your bones,' she said. 'This will, instead, show up the soft tissue in your body, so we can tell if the internal organs are as they should be. What I'm going to do is give you an injection in the arm with a dye, then shortly after we'll take a series of X-rays. Okay?'

I nodded. She walked over to a table and came back with a small dish upon which was a needle and a piece of cotton wool soaked in antiseptic.

'When I give you the injection you might feel a bit dizzy or hot for a few seconds. This will pass, so don't worry. Just stay lying where you are and you'll be alright. Can you roll up your sleeve?'

I did as she asked.

'Goodness! You're as thin as an eight-year-old boy I had in here earlier today.'

I was surprised to hear such a comment considering the radiographer must have seen people in all stages of illness as a normal part of her job, and I didn't find it amusing in the slightest. It certainly didn't make me feel better about myself, but I made no comment and let her get on with what she had to do.

The needle had barely been withdrawn when I had the most unnerving sensation of heat rushing throughout my body. It was over within a few seconds and, shortly after-wards, the radiographer began to take her images. The whole process was completed quickly.

'How will I get the results?' I asked, as I sat up on the table.

'If you go to your GP in about a week, he'll have them by then,' she answered.

Less than twenty minutes later I was dressed, out of the hospital and on my way to college to catch up on what was left of the morning's classes. My lunch break would be spent working.

It was towards the end of April when I went to see the GP to get the results of the IVP, which I had since found out stood for 'intravenous pyelogram'. I felt weary to the bone. If this test proved negative I doubted that the GP would send me for any more. My options, along with my energy, were feeble.

'You can go in, Mr Paris,' said the receptionist.

I stood up slowly and walked down the corridor with a feeling of dread and moments later I was sitting opposite the GP. He didn't speak for a while, so we sat in silence and I thought we were going to have a repeat performance of the previous visits. Then he spoke.

'I have the results of your X-ray from the hospital ... they show you have a blockage in the tube that leads out of your right kidney. This has meant that, over a period of time, your kidney has become increasingly enlarged. There is little doubt this has been the cause of your pain and ill-health.'

Double six.

It was as simple as that.

The GP took a piece of paper and drew the outline of a man.

'Your kidneys are here, low down on each side,' he said, drawing what looked like two fried eggs. 'The function of the kidneys is to cleanse the blood and get rid of liquid waste, which they do through a tube to your bladder. However, because the tube from your right kidney has become partially blocked, the build-up of pressure has led to it becoming extended.'

He made one of the fried eggs about twice the size of the other.

'It can be cured, though you'll have to go into hospital for an operation. It's not a life-and-death procedure, but it is a major one. You'll be in for about ten days and will then have to convalesce for several weeks after that.'

'It's taken so long to find this out and it needed only a simple test. Why?'

He looked uncomfortable, but said nothing so we sat through another long silence.

'Will the kidney return to normal after the operation?' I asked.

'Not entirely, though it should reduce in size a bit once the pressure is released. There is a chance that it might have to be removed.'

I stared at him in shock. This was the result of boarding so many wrong trains. I should have been stronger earlier on and not allowed so much time to be wasted.

'Many people live completely ordinary lives with only one

kidney,' he said, suddenly becoming animated, chatty and quite out of character. 'That's not something to worry about. I can get you into the Watford General or, if you like, I can probably arrange for you to have the operation in the North-East. It's up to you. I could ring now.'

He rested his hand on the telephone to demonstrate he was willing to make the call at that very moment.

'What about my exams?'

'When are they?'

'June.'

'Well, you would certainly be out before then, though you won't have recovered fully. You could have the operation after your exams, but that means carrying on for some time. It's up to you.'

I couldn't think straight and wanted out of the room, into the fresh air.

'Take some time to think it over. I can get you into hospital quickly even if you tell me your answer in a few days.'

I stood up.

'I'll be in touch,' I said and walked out, leaving him with his drawing of fried eggs.

My intention upon leaving the surgery was to go to college. Instead, I headed to Cassiobury Park and out into the countryside. I was rarely warm these days and shivered even though the day wasn't that cold. I was angry, but as much with myself as anyone else. For months I had been blown around the corridors of medicine with little more control over my destiny than a leaf in the wind. Could I have done things differently? Had I really been so powerless?

The experts had all been convinced that the problem lay within their specialist field. The rheumatologist was so certain it was my spine that he had put me on traction; the osteopath so positive the pain was from a bulging disc that he wanted me to have surgery; the hypnotherapist so confident it was caused by tension. Only the Harley Street specialist had admitted he didn't know what was wrong.

My weakness came largely from ignorance, not of medicine, which I couldn't be expected to know, but of the procedures of medicine. I hadn't known about second opinions, about changing your GP because you had no faith, about the right to refuse a treatment, and not then to be dismissed or denied other help for the same problem.

I had been brought up to believe in the demigod, and the idea of challenging one had for so long been unthinkable. But they were men and women, as likely to make mistakes in life as the rest of us. It had taken a while for me to stand up and say, 'No'; too long, in hindsight.

Now, I had to make a very big decision.

Chapter Seventeen

I rang the surgery the next day.

'I want to have the operation as soon as possible and in Watford so that I can take my exams afterwards,' I said, once put through to the GP.

'Right. Ring me back this afternoon and I'll have a date for you.'

When I called later he told me to go to the Watford General hospital on 12th May. The only person I had spoken to prior to ringing the surgery was my course tutor, Mr Goode, to ask whether the college would award me the HND if I didn't take my final exams. He confirmed that they would.

Next, I had the task of telling Mam and Dad, who had not known about the latest round of tests. It was obvious that Mam had picked up the telephone before she even spoke, because there was always a long pause and then a tiny voice would say hesitantly 'hellooo?'

Mam was never really comfortable with telephones and always answered as if she expected the caller to be Lucifer ringing from the Underworld. When she discovered it wasn't, Mam was always delighted to chat, but the next time you rang she would be back to wondering if it was someone calling from a very hot place.

'Hello, Mam. Some good news,' I said, trying to sound positive. 'They've found out what's wrong with me.'

'Oh, that's marvellous, dear.'

Having heard the explanation, she expressed her concern

that the operation would be so far from the family. It was a point that also worried me, for I would be relying on the friends made locally during my first year, not only to visit and bring me the occasional grape, but also to do my washing and buy anything I might need.

The next few days were spent arranging for people on the course to provide me with notes from all the lectures I would miss while in hospital and immediately afterwards. There wasn't a lot I could do except cram as much revision as possible into the time that was left.

There was a barn dance that Saturday and I felt well enough to go along with Rose and Babs. It was a big dance and there were a lot of faces I had never seen before. During the interval I got talking to a very attractive woman at the table where they were selling records and tapes. She was a similar age to me and it turned out we shared the same interests in folk music. She was a doctor.

It was the first time I had ever met one socially and she seemed no different from any of the other dancers in the room. We got on well. When I returned to my own group there was a bit of leg-pulling about my 'new friend'. It was all in good humour and forgotten as soon as the music started. However, I did manage one dance with her later on.

I couldn't decide how fast I wanted the days to pass, but the evening finally came when I had to pack my bag, ready to go into hospital the following morning. The main items were textbooks for my revision, covering subjects from printing technology to accountancy and company law. The only non-text book I allowed myself was a copy of *The Hobbit*. When everything was packed I went downstairs to play chess with Paul. You would have thought he might have let me win just once.

The walk from Gammons Lane was the loneliest journey I had ever made, and each reluctant step was taken at half my normal speed. When I eventually found the ward, a nurse showed me to a bed and told me to put on my pyjamas.

There were several empty beds, including those either side of my own. I opened my case and began to unpack, stacking the books neatly in the locker and arranging items so that they could be reached easily. When all this was done I undressed, put on my pyjamas then laid out my clothes in the now empty suitcase for Mr and Mrs Wilcox to take away that evening. I shoved the case under the bed, sat down and waited, not really sure what I was meant to do.

After about ten minutes one of the other patients came over to introduce himself. He had arrived shortly before me and was also going into theatre the next day, although he expected to be in hospital for less than a week. I seemed to bump into people from Scotland wherever I went, and Bill looked like he had celebrated his seventieth birthday a long time ago. He had come in to sort out, 'that trouble doon below that we aw git when ye git tae my age.' At least, I think that's what he said.

The atmosphere was completely different from that on the traction ward, and much of this was down to the state of the patients. Those who had recently had operations were too poorly to feel like making conversation, while those waiting to go to theatre were subdued and keeping to their own private thoughts. One or two wandered around, at the in-between stage; over their surgery, yet not quite well enough to go home.

As Bill and I chatted I saw a figure walking towards us and my mouth opened in disbelief. The white coat did nothing to hide the extremely attractive figure. It was the woman I had met at the dance. Bill made a timely retreat.

'Hello,' she said brightly.

'Hello, Ann,' I said, feeling suddenly even more miserable. 'What are you doing here?'

'I'm the ward doctor. I won't ask you why you're here because I've already read your notes.'

She sat down on the bed next to me.

'Take off your top. I need to listen to your chest.'

I took off my pyjama top and she placed the cold end of the stethoscope on my chest. I felt extremely conscious of how emaciated my body was.

'You'll have to give a blood sample later on. The nurse will come and get you. You're due at theatre around eleven tomorrow morning, so you can have lunch and supper, and drink until midnight, but you mustn't have anything after that.'

She filled me in on several other points then finished by saying that she would 'see me in theatre', before standing up and walking out of the ward.

I didn't feel like getting into bed so put on my dressing gown and slippers, picked up a book on the manufacture of paper and went to the day room at the end of the ward. Bill and another patient were already chatting and the idea of studying was soon forgotten. About an hour later a nurse stuck her head around the door and told me to give a blood sample. She gave me instructions on where to go and I set off down the corridor in search of the right room.

At lunchtime I ended up at a table with four other men, two of whom were due for operations the next day, and two who had obviously had theirs, because they carried little plastic bags. Each bag had a tube leading out of the top, which disappeared somewhere under their dressing gowns. I wasn't too keen to know any of the finer details.

The food was alright, but none of us seemed to have much appetite. We chatted about our various problems and there were little bouts of nervous laughter when someone made a half-funny comment. After lunch I joined a few men to play cards until visiting time later that afternoon.

It seemed even the visitors were subdued, and they huddled in small groups around beds to talk in whispers. Maybe people had problems they didn't want others to hear of. I didn't have anyone coming to see me, so lay on my bed with the book on paper manufacturing. After half an hour I was still no further than page three.

It was only apprehension. Once the operation was over I would be able to apply my mind totally to studying once more and would catch up on what had been missed. After all, you didn't have to be on your feet to read a book. All this time lying around could be turned to my advantage.

Tea and supper followed the same pattern as lunch. I was lying on top of the bed in my dressing gown when my visitors arrived, carrying the mandatory fruit and soft drinks. I had met my landlords at the folk dance class, where they were long-time members, so had known them socially before moving to Gammons Lane. She was called Mandy and was happy for me to call her that. He was Geoff, but once I lodged with them he felt I should refer to him as 'Mr Wilcox'.

It was a bit of a strange situation. I had to stop calling him Geoff and start calling him by his surname, even if a group of us had gathered at someone's house for drinks after a Saturday night dance. However, it didn't bother me and we all got on well.

As we chatted, I thought what a kind elderly couple they

were and how grateful I was to them for taking me in, as the lodgings the college had arranged had been a terrible place. I had spent the first term there and had never known such cold, while having a toilet at the bottom of the garden had been a bizarre concept to someone brought up in a block of flats.

I had shared a room with another lad from my course. We had no heating except a small radiator, which could be switched on for an hour at most each day. On one particular wild night we put it on before going to the pub and when we returned the radiator had vanished.

Yes, if Mr Wilcox had wanted me to call him Sir Geoff, salute, then pipe him into the bedroom every morning when he brought my cereal and toast, I would have been more than happy to do so. He asked me several times during the visit if I needed anything brought, but there was nothing I wanted other than to have the operation over with.

When they had gone, taking away my suitcase, I joined the card game that started soon after the last of the visitors left. But our minds were not on it and dealing was interspersed with talk of families and how everyone was looking forward to returning home. Tension hung around the table like fog on a windless day.

I left the table and wandered up and down the ward, in and out of the day room, picking up books and magazines then returning them almost immediately to the pile. The tea trolley came around shortly after nine and I drank several mugs as this would be the last liquid I could have for a while. Eventually, men began to make their way to the washroom. I dragged out cleaning my teeth for as long as possible and the ward was in semi-darkness when I went back in, with most patients already in their beds.

143

I climbed into mine, pulled the sheets up to my chin and looked at the ceiling. It was pointless to even consider going to sleep, so I simply lay there trying not to imagine what would happen in the morning. The ward became quieter and the only movement was a nurse checking on a few patients. The dials on the clock reached the half hour, the hour and the half hour again. It was well after midnight when I started to drift off. The last thing I remember thinking was that it was Friday the thirteenth.

Chapter Eighteen

I woke at dawn and from that moment onwards the minutes had dragged like they had never dragged since being invented. By nine-thirty two patients had already been wheeled out of the ward. Around ten o'clock a nurse handed me a gown to put on, gave me a pre-med and told me not to get out of bed again. I gathered this was supposed to make me feel sleepy and relaxed. It didn't work.

A few of the other guys had spoken to me earlier on, but once the nurse had given me the injection they left me alone, no doubt assuming that I would be feeling drowsy. I kept counting the tiles on the ceiling, over and over. Where was the vicar? I could have done with a visit now.

Shortly before eleven I saw a trolley being wheeled along the ward and knew it was for me. The porter was whistling as if there wasn't a problem in the whole world, while the nurse looked like she should still be at school.

'Right then, Philip. We're just going to take you down to theatre,' he said, throwing back the bed clothes. 'If you'll just move across ... that's it.'

They covered me with a blanket and the next moment I was being wheeled feet first along the ward.

'You'll be alright, son,' shouted someone.

I couldn't see who it was so stuck a thumb in the air then we were in the corridor. It was just like on television, when they placed a camera on a trolley and all there was on the screen were ceiling lights flashing past overhead, and occasionally faces looming into and out of view.

One of the wheels needed fixing and we were accompanied by a *click, click, click.* Every minute detail of the journey was being etched into my mind; each smell and sound. I closed my eyes to block them out. After a few minutes we went over a bump and came to a halt. Then there was a different motion. We were going up.

'Open your eyes, man. What are you afraid of?' said the porter jokingly.

I looked up.

'There's nothing to be scared of. You won't know anything about it.'

'If you like, you can lie here instead of me.'

It was meant to be funny, but there was no humour in my voice so the joke fell flat. I was beginning to feel light-headed.

'You'll be okay. Next time I see you, you'll be sitting up in bed wondering what made you so worried.'

I managed a weak smile, not believing a word of it.

'Tell me what you're concerned about and I bet I can put your mind at rest.'

There was no chance to reply because the lift stopped, the doors opened and we were once more moving along a corridor, lights flashing overhead ... *click, click, click.* We entered a small side room and stopped.

'You'll be alright,' said the porter, patting my shoulder before leaving.

The nurse was still at the head of the trolley and hadn't spoken during the trip from the ward. I think the pre-med must have finally been taking effect because I was becoming quite disorientated. However, I could see there were others in the room; medical people in uniforms.

How many had I seen since all this started? Bright white,

navy blue, pale blue uniforms; nurses, sisters, doctors, orderlies, cleaners ... It all began when I thought a muscle had been strained while playing tennis with Paul; the day Babs and I had attended the born-again Christian meeting. How long ago was that?

'Philip. Philip.'

I stared into a woman's face, very near to mine. It was a nice, kind, motherly sort of face. Who was she?

'I'm just going to give you a little injection in the arm to put you to sleep, and you'll know nothing more until you wake up back on the ward all better.'

I closed my eyes again, partly owing to the strange feeling of detachment that had fallen over me, but also because I didn't want to see what was happening around me. I was going down in the lift. Down ... down ... deeper. It was a lovely day in the garden. The sun was shining and so hot that it made me want to lie on the grass, relax and forget about everything.

Reeelaaax. That's what the hypnotherapist used to say, drawing it out so that it sounded like two words. Relax. That's what the osteopath had said when I was on the table and he was going to twist my body, put the disc back in place. They were all in the garden. But it was my garden. They shouldn't have been there.

'Try your hand at throwing the dice. Double six wins every time ...'

'Feeling stressed? Just lie on this couch ...'

'Roll up and get your traction here ...'

A man walked up to me.

'Here, have one of these.'

He dropped a small white pill into my hand.

'Have this now, and you don't pay until later on ...'

'Alright,' I said and popped it into my mouth.

Noooo. Not *that* train.

Music, dancing, marching in the kilt; studying, hoping, aiming to be the best; swimming up and down the pool a 100,000 times; running through the factory; white medicine down the toilet; sleeping on a board; pain and sickness; frustration and despair … dead eyes staring from a wasted body.

Someone reached down into the dark pit I had fallen into and took hold of my hand to pull me out. It was the tiny nurse who had helped to wheel me from the ward. I hung on to her as if she was my closest friend in the whole world, my only salvation. She smiled, stroking my brow with her free hand, stopping me from falling back into the darkness.

There was something wet and cold on my other arm, then a sharp sting and everything began to merge and fade. I was in the lift and it was freefalling. Fast. Fast. Plummeting into the deep so that the levels clicked like the wheel on the trolley. *Click, click, click.*

I hung on so tightly to the little nurse, but in my grasp her hand turned to mist and, having no substance, it slipped silently through my fingers.

Chapter Nineteen

Someone had left a window open and a soft breeze blew gently across my face; a whispering breeze, with a thousand stories to tell. It had told me so much while asleep: tales of adventure; great secrets that must not be repeated. Now I was awake the words were carried away on the wind and no longer clear enough for me to catch.

There was another sound, a harsher, gabbling type of noise, which I couldn't understand. A small boy appeared by the bed and looked down at me. Everything was so terribly confused. I was lying on my side in a hospital bed and there was a boy standing beside me. I could just about remember why I was there … but him?

Then I realised. Of course, it was visiting time. The noise was caused by dozens of people talking. And if it was visiting time that meant it was evening.

'Eeeevening,' repeated the breeze, so near it felt inside my head. Was it all finally over? I lay very still and tried to concentrate on picking up conversations, but only made out the occasional phrase.

'Oh, I'm so pleased you're better …'

'That doctor seems nice …'

I wanted to call for a nurse, not for any particular reason, but it was impossible to speak. No matter how hard I tried to say something to the boy who was only a few feet away, I couldn't utter a single word. Then he was gone and there was no one. I tried to move, but discovered that not one part of my body would respond an inch, not even my head.

'Don't lisssten to them,' said the whispering breeze. 'Lisssten to meee. Go back to sleep, and lisssten to meee.'

The wind promised to tell me more stories of adventure, and secrets that only we would know.

Upon waking, the ward was silent apart from my constant companion, which blew so softly across my cheek it felt as though caressing fingers were stroking me affectionately; like the nurse before I had lost consciousness. Perhaps that's what I was remembering.

My right side hurt like blazes and if I couldn't move my arms or legs before, I didn't want to now, because the slightest attempt at changing position resulted in searing pain. I lay quietly, waiting. There was nothing more to do. Time passed. People occasionally walked nearby. Then someone bent over me, so that her head was near to mine.

'You're back on the ward now, all safe and sound in your bed. Everything went very well, so you've nothing to worry about,' she said.

The nurse reached over, put her hand on my face and started to take something off my head. I didn't understand what she was doing and it was only when her hands came back into view that I realised I had been wearing an oxygen mask. She draped the mask over a nearby cylinder, which I hadn't noticed before, and the whispering breeze disappeared in an instant.

'How are you feeling?' said asked, pushing back a few locks of hair that had fallen over my brow.

I caught the scent of her perfume, so unlike the sterile smells of the hospital. I couldn't believe the enormous effort of will it took to speak and in the end didn't say anything.

'Are you in a lot of pain?'

I replied with a grimace.

'Lie there quietly. I'll return soon with something for you.'

It seemed extraordinary to me just how helpless I felt.

'Mr Paris, I'm going to give you something to take away the pain.'

The speaker was wearing a navy uniform and I guessed she was the sister. The nurse who had left a short while earlier was by her side and between them they pulled back the bedclothes. I was wearing the gown in which I had been taken to theatre.

There appeared to be a lot of tubes entering and leaving places where tubes had no right to be, but I couldn't work out where they were going and didn't care. The two women moved me around a bit and the pain became much worse, which didn't seem to be the aim of the exercise.

'I'm going to give you an injection in your thigh, okay?' said the sister, fetching a needle from a small tray lying on the locker nearby.

I just wanted her to get on with it. She wiped a part of my thigh with a piece of damp cotton wool then there was a sting as the needle was inserted, but it was one grain of sand in a thousand compared to the pain around my side. When this was done, they pulled up the bedclothes.

'If you need anything during the night, just press this buzzer,' said the nurse, who laid a cable with a plunger on the end next to my head.

Then they were gone. Was it really over? I had no idea if the kidney had been removed or not, but at that moment it didn't seem to matter. My awareness of what was going on around me diminished, and I became conscious of nothing further than the tubes leading out from under the bedclothes; conscious of nothing beyond my own body ... outside my head and the thoughts held within it ... then nothing.

The ward was filled with a bright light and there was the noise of footsteps, people talking and objects being wheeled across the floor. I hadn't a clue what time it was, only that it was morning and I felt like death. My side was hurting like crazy again. In fact, my body ached all over. There was no sign of the buzzer.

The strange thing was that my greatest need was not something for the pain. It was for a drink of water. Such thirst was beyond anything I had experienced. Inch by painful inch I turned my head to look at the water jug on my locker. But no matter how hard I tried there was no way I could even get my arm out from under the blankets, never mind reach the jug.

I would have given so much for one glass, half a glass, a mouthful. To have a container so close was torment indeed. Ten, twenty, thirty minutes went by. The sunlight glanced off the water and when a trolley was wheeled nearby, the liquid danced and sparkled. I could have cried with the need for some.

I started offering deals with the big man above if He would only send someone, even just to moisten my lips. First, I promised to do all the things I should, but rarely got around to, and not do things that I shouldn't but did. Then, I mentally gave up my possessions, donating them to the worthiest charities, until I owned nothing other than the hospital gown. And that wasn't mine. Still nothing happened.

Well, why should He bother? I wasn't particularly religious. Why should He think about me when I didn't think about Him, and when there were millions of people around the world in far greater need? So I took back my possessions and decided to do whatever I wanted when I had recovered. And I wouldn't be bothering Him again for all the good my pleading did.

That was when the angel appeared.

At first, I didn't know he was an angel because he was disguised very cleverly as a bald, middle-aged bloke, whose girth was escaping over the top of his pyjama bottoms, which didn't actually come anywhere near his pyjama top. I had never seen him before.

'How are you feeling?' asked the patient.

There was no way I could reply, so simply raised my eyebrows.

'Well, it's all over now.'

My eyebrows rose higher. Then he said those words.

'Do you want a drink?'

The expression on my face must have said it all. The man filled a tumbler from the jug and slipped a tubby hand gently under my head to raise it. He held the glass to my lips. It was the best drink I have ever tasted before or since.

'Take it easy,' he said, when I gulped the water too quickly for my own good and spluttered some of it back out. When the glass was empty he put it back on the locker and produced a tissue with which he wiped my chin and cheeks, until only the pillow was a little damp.

The kindness of this act was not lost upon me, even when I felt so ill, for the man wasn't a doctor or nurse or someone working in the hospital. He didn't have the licence to touch in the way that medical people did. He was just some bloke on the ward ... or maybe not. Several days later, when I was well enough to take note of what was going on around me, I looked out for the patient, but I never saw him again. However, I will always remember that act of kindness ... and the glass of water.

The pain from the operation returned with a vengeance and relief came shortly afterwards with another injection in the thigh. The morning wore on like treacle. It must have been around lunchtime when I saw them walking down the ward; an old nurse followed by a young one carrying a brown plastic basin and a large towel. They stopped at my bed and closed the curtains.

'We've come to give you a bed bath, Mr Paris. It won't take very long,' said the older of the two.

A bed bath?

They must be joking. Maybe I was hallucinating. At that moment in my life, I felt as close to dying as I ever had and the prospect of two women sponging me down was very high on the list of activities I didn't want to be involved in.

Were they really serious?

They were. Before I had the opportunity to react in any way, they pulled the bedclothes away and set about my legs with sponges and clothes, which they replenished regularly from the basin of hot water. When this task had been accomplished and my spindly legs dried by the large fluffy towel, they took down the top part of my gown so they could get to my arms and chest.

Several minutes, dips, splashes, squeezes and rubs later my top half was also clean and dry. There was only one bit left to do. The young nurse lifted the gown while the older one worked up a good lather on her sponge. Then she turned to me.

'Do you want to do this bit or do you want me to?'

I couldn't have cared if the Archbishop of Canterbury had done it. I just wanted them to leave me alone. I was sure they had both 'seen it all before', but perhaps there was some hospital rule about giving the patient a choice. However, my brain was operating as effectively as a mashed potato and it took an age before I could get my mouth to give an answer. During this lull in the proceedings we all looked at each other in silence; me, the two nurses, the sponge and old Tom.

'You,' I eventually managed to whisper.

The next moment, my nether regions were attacked by the hot soapy sponge, which was applied with rather too much enthusiasm and elbow grease. When the job was done, they tucked me up once more and I drifted off to sleep.

I wanted a pee. Despite all the other discomforts beating my body without mercy, as the afternoon wore on having a pee became an all-consuming priority. I managed to attract the attention of a passing nurse and she brought a bottle, closing the curtains around me. It was no good. I had a complete mental block about urinating into a small container while several people were talking just the other side of a thin curtain. It must have been my rather Victorian upbringing.

The nurse came back. She was a sturdy lass and I asked if she would help me get to the washroom. Bearing in mind that a few hours earlier I hadn't had the strength to lift my arm from under the blankets, this was an undertaking on a phenomenal scale. To her credit she didn't argue the point, which I had expected, and manoeuvred me into a standing position, having first put my slippers on for me. I had to carry the drainage bag, which gave her one arm to hold me upright and one to wheel the drip stand.

Off we set at the speed of an arthritic slug. The focus of my entire consciousness was on the next step and never in my life had I needed such determination or concentration to perform a task. However, as we moved along, step by wobbly step, I became aware of men shouting. Not for an instant could I risk taking my eyes off the floor but, yes, voices with strong Geordie accents were calling out and cheering from every direction.

'Good for you, son.'

'Go on, lad, you can do it.'

Someone started clapping. *Clapping!* Then others joined in. It seemed that everyone was following our progress closely. This was no longer a walk down the ward. It was Bannister's four-minute-mile. It was Armstrong's first steps on the moon. It was madness. But every patient on that ward was united in a sudden spirit of male bonding as they urged me to claim my right as a man to have a pee while standing in front of a urinal.

'Well done, son.'

'You're doing fine.'

The calls continued until the door closed behind us in the washroom. Never before had someone heading for a pee stirred men's hearts to such passion.

The pain came back, but there were no further injections and instead I was given tablets. Then, ever so slowly, evening turned into night and I became quite ill. Two years of deteriorating health had left me with little in the way of reserves for a major operation.

Having slept for a lot of the day I now lay awake in the semi-darkness. Night-time became a nightmare. The nurses came and went, taking my pulse, checking my temperature. Faceless, shadowy figures moving in silence. How could they not see the monsters sitting on top of my bed?

They kept telling me the stories I most feared to hear; reminding me of scenes I didn't want to remember, like the hundreds of dead cockroaches I walked on once when I went into a flat in the block that had been sprayed. The scene was unimaginable. They covered every square inch of every flat surface; tables, kitchen tops, sinks, chairs, and fell out in piles if you opened a cupboard door. Now and again one would twitch its legs. Difficult things to kill, cockroaches. They were there that night, in the hospital bed.

The moans of patients who had recently been to theatre occasionally filled the ward, and at times someone cried out more loudly than the others. Then I realised it was me. More silent figures by the bed. Why didn't they speak, instead of just checking my pulse? I wanted to move, but the tubes were restricting and it hurt to change position. Never had a night passed so slowly.

The next morning was little better, though the monsters had gone. They didn't like daylight. Everyone knew that. Shortly before lunchtime two nurses appeared and said they were going to move me nearer the entrance so the night staff could keep an eye on me more easily.

I was wheeled along the ward in my bed. We passed the patient whose place I was taking as he headed in the opposite direction. When I was settled into my new position between the end of the ward and the second bed along, the locker containing my books, toiletries and other possessions was moved next to me.

It was Sunday. I remembered early in the afternoon. Rose was due to visit although if I had known how ill I was going to feel I wouldn't have asked anyone to come for a few more days. She walked past the bed when that afternoon's visitors were allowed in, but I couldn't do anything except wait for her to find me.

The conversation was extremely one-sided as it still required a huge amount of energy to speak. The silences

157

were broken by Rose remembering some bit of news about someone at the dance group, or something that had interested her, or that she thought I would be keen to hear. It must have been a boring encounter for her.

Shortly after she left it was discovered that I had developed an infection, and so began the first of what were to be twice-daily injections. Later on, when I felt better, one of my main occupations was wondering who was going to give me the next injection, because this experience ranged from not feeling anything to being convinced that the nurse was training to throw the javelin at the Olympics.

But all this was to come and, as the Sunday wore on, I continued to feel detached from what was going on around me. Paul came that evening and as he was a quiet lad the visit was memorable for being almost without conversation. Still, his visit was appreciated. When he left he promised to return later in the week, and I promised to be more sociable.

I told the monsters to bugger off that night and they largely left me alone. Maybe it was the extra light that filtered in from the corridor. When I woke on the Monday I was surprised at how much better I felt; still pretty awful, but not ill in the way I had been. During the morning a nurse brought a basin of hot water, along with soap, sponge and towel and then drew the curtains around my bed before leaving me to wash myself.

It was more than a bit tricky, but before the water had gone completely cold I was clean (sort of) and dry, had changed the hospital gown for my own pyjamas and felt almost human again. Apart from the first day I had not had anything to do with the other patients and now that I looked more approachable, a couple of them came over to speak. This included Bill the Scotsman.

'How are you feeling today?' he asked.

'A lot better thanks,' I replied; the longest sentence I had spoken since Friday morning.

'Aye. You were looking a bit poorly over the weekend, but you have more colour in your cheeks this morning.'

We chatted on until lunchtime when Bill left to join the others around the tables in the centre of the ward. It struck me that I hadn't eaten for nearly four days. Four days! I started to feel hungry, but my decision to try something turned out to be extremely unwise as one mouthful made me feel dreadfully sick and I had to push the plate away. I felt guilty at wasting an entire meal.

Not long afterwards one of the nurses came to give me an injection. I swore under my breath as she approached. It was the javelin thrower. I wouldn't have been surprised if she had taken a run towards me before launching herself, needle held at arm's length, straight at my right buttock.

I manoeuvred my pyjama bottoms to expose a small patch of posterior, while the nurse pulled the curtains closed. She was behind me, so was out of sight, which made the anticipation of what was to come even worse.

Bloody hell.

She withdrew the needle and I covered myself up.

'Sorry,' she said. 'I haven't done it right. I'll have to do it again.'

I could just turn sufficiently to see her face. In fairness, she didn't look like a sadist, but then you could never tell. Reluctantly, I pulled down the pyjama bottom again. Boy, she certainly found the same spot. No problem with accuracy there. Wasn't there any justice in the world? She withdrew the needle and I pulled up my bottoms, before rubbing the spot gently with my hand. There was a pause.

'I'm really sorry ... I still haven't done it properly. I'll have to do it again.'

Although it hurt to do so, I moved around to face her.

'Again!' I said aghast.

'Sorry,' she said.

Somehow, I'm not sure she was. I turned over, pulled down my bottoms and she found that exact same place. I had gone through the whole of the operation and everything surrounding it without having a moist eye, but there were tears in them when she stuck in that needle for a third time!

Ann sat on my bed during her ward round to chat about how I was getting on. I felt a slight one-upmanship on the other men, because they all called her 'doctor' and I never let on that I had met her only once before, about two weeks earlier. She said I was making a good recovery, apart from the infection, and I was at last able to find out if the kidney had been removed during the operation. It was a relief to learn it was still there and that the blockage in the tube had been cleared without any complications.

After she had moved on I asked one of the more able patients if he would wheel the mobile telephone to the side of my bed and I rang Mam and Dad. They seemed like a long way away, which I suppose they were. I left them to spread the word to the rest of the family that I was on the mend. That night, with the aid of a sleeping tablet, I slept soundly.

On the Tuesday I felt amazingly better, particularly considering how ill I had been at the weekend. I managed to eat some toast without feeling sick, the first food since the previous Thursday. A nurse came to remove the drip so the stand, bag and tube were no longer a part of me.

When I saw the length of the needle that had been inserted into my forearm I was glad I had been unconscious when it had been put in. She put a small sticking plaster over the hole. Of course, I still had the drainage bag, which had a tube entering my side near the end of the operation site, so had to carry this with me wherever I went.

Shortly after, the same nurse came back with a basin containing a sponge, soap and hot water for my morning wash. The tiny mirror fitted to the inside of my electric razor only showed a small part of my face and I had to move this about while shaving. I discovered later that several bits had been missed, but it was my first shave since Thursday morning and felt good, regardless of thoroughness.

When I was clean and the water in the basin less so, I changed into another pair of pyjamas, putting the used ones into a carrier bag ready for Babs that afternoon. I lay back on the bed, exhausted. However, I had only ever seen part of the scar, which disappeared around my back, and my curiosity grew. Climbing slowly out of bed, I picked up the drainage bag and set off to the washroom.

It was occupied so I washed my hands at the sink until the patient left then I walked up to the long mirror at the end of the room and, putting down the bag, lifted my pyjama top. The red angry line that snaked around my right side was about ten inches in length and looked as though someone had tried to rub it out with lots of little lines.

It was a strange feeling, because although it had been done to make me better, somehow it seemed an affront to my body. Oh well, that put paid to my modelling career. I picked up the bag, but before moving away something about my face made me hesitate. In fact, it was the first time I had stood in front of a mirror since before the operation.

My hair was now pretty disgusting and stuck up into the air in small clumps, while my drawn cheeks, sunken eyes and pale complexion were worse than ever. However, that wasn't what caught my attention. There was a difference in my face that at first I couldn't put my finger on. But upon examining it more closely, the reason suddenly came to me. I was no longer haunted. The expression of despair had gone.

Physically, I looked bloody awful. But the other part of me, which housed the sparkle, humour and hope ... that had returned. It was in the eyes. The frightening brown pools of dead water in the disused quarry had gone.

I smiled.

What a pathetic sight, my pyjamas flopping around my shrunken frame so much that the bottoms were in danger of falling around my ankles at any moment. I was an absolute wreck. So I smiled some more and went back to bed with a heart lighter than it had been for longer than I could remember.

Chapter Twenty

The old man looked down at me with sad eyes; eyes that had seen a thousand wounded bodies, which had shared a lifetime's tears. I didn't know who he was. He just appeared by the bed, early that Wednesday afternoon. I was sitting up, propped by several pillows and reading *The Hobbit*. My legs were tucked underneath me so that the blankets were flat until they reached my knees before covering me up to my waist.

He didn't speak and I made a wild guess he was from a local church, or from some group of people who wandered around hospitals and spoke to patients who looked as though they needed company. The book lay in my lap as I returned his gaze, my face frozen in a half-smile waiting for him to say something. Finally, he broke the silence, just as my cheeks were beginning to twitch.

'How are you?'

His voice, like his eyes, was full of sorrow and concern. For a moment I wasn't quite sure how to respond. I had been feeling quite perky, but was now beginning to wonder if I had missed something and should actually be much worse.

'Well ... not too bad, thank you.'

Another long silence followed. He looked constantly between me and the bed as if he wasn't quite certain which one to speak to. If he did this day after day, he certainly didn't have a lot to offer in the way of conversation. An image of him walking around wards, depressing perfectly contented people, flashed into my head.

'Are you comfortable here ... in the hospital?'

The memory of lunchtime's shepherd's pie came to mind, but I dismissed this as being particularly ungrateful and instead replied that everyone had been very kind. I didn't mention the javelin thrower. He nodded his head slowly in agreement. My spirits were sinking fast. Perhaps he had been sent to tell me some bad news and wasn't sure how to do it. There was definitely something he knew, which I didn't.

'When did you have the operation?' he asked, his gaze falling on the bed as if his grief was so great he could no longer look me in the eye.

'Friday,' I answered.

'Friday! That's unbelievable. Absolutely unbelievable,' he raved. 'Here you are sitting up in bed, talking and reading and looking so well, and you had the operation only on Friday.'

On and on he went, his mood now completely the opposite of only seconds earlier. There was no doubt about it; I must have appeared far worse than I felt and was considering if a doctor should be called for urgently when he suddenly went very quiet, his sad eyes once more on the bed.

'So, what happened exactly?'

'Well,' I said, 'it all started with a pain in the small of my back.'

'Your back?' he gasped, putting a hand to his mouth.

'My back,' I confirmed, wondering which one of us I should actually call a doctor for. 'I've had an operation near my kidney.'

I hadn't seen what was coming. Just hadn't seen it at all.

'You mean ... you mean, you've still got your legs?'

164

With these words, he bent down and lifted the blankets so that he could peer at my legs, which were still tucked neatly underneath me. The penny finally dropped and although I opened my mouth to speak, I couldn't think of a single thing to say.

He let go of the blankets and looked at me with such a disappointed expression that I felt like a fraud, as if I had deliberately set out to trick him; a wicked, cruel thing to do to a kind old gentleman, who had given up his time to visit people in hospital. I stared at him, speechless, while he went a very unusual shade of pink. After a few moments with neither of us speaking, he mumbled something I didn't catch, turned around and walked quickly out of the ward.

For some time I sat motionless, trying to work out if it was me, him or both of us who were slightly mad. The thought that I had just been talking with someone, who was under the impression throughout our entire conversation ... Quite to the surprise of the patient in the next bed I let out something akin to a shriek, sending my copy of *The Hobbit* slithering across the floor.

Then I completely lost control and, even though it hurt to do so, I laughed and laughed while the bed rocked and creaked, and tears cascaded down my face. A few patients watched on, bemused, while more than one passing nurse slowed down to see what was happening. I could offer no explanation for I was quite incapable of speaking. When Babs arrived shortly afterwards, she found me helpless, a wad of tissues in each hand.

'Whatever has happened?' she asked, not at all sure what to make of my behaviour.

It took several minutes to tell her through tears, laughs and cries of 'Oh my side, my side', the events that had taken place. When I finished, she pulled a hanky out from her handbag and fell into a complete state of hysterics.

For the entire visit we hardly spoke, as every time we managed to calm ourselves we only had to look at each other to start all over again. When Babs left I could hear her laughing down the corridor and, I fancied, out in the car park. If only that man had known how much good he had done me he would have realised there was no reason whatsoever for him to feel embarrassed at his mistake.

Every day I was improving and although still very weak I decided on the Thursday that it was time to start revising for my exams. After breakfast, which was eaten at the table with the others, I pulled a textbook out of my locker and settled down in bed to begin at chapter one, which explained about the different ingredients used to make an ink.

I read the first few pages, went back to the beginning and later on did the same thing again. This was information that I had understood months ago, but now the words were almost meaningless. Putting down the book, I poured a glass of water from the jug on the locker. Ever since the day after the operation it had been a great pleasure to pour a glass of water. I began again with even greater vigour.

An hour later, I closed the book, still no further than those initial pages. It was hopeless. I had simply had no concept as to how the operation would affect me. My ability to concentrate, such as it was, had been erased completely, like my memory. Not only was I unable to take in a few new facts, I couldn't remember the ones I used to know.

Details that could once be recited without hesitation were like mist at the edges of my mind and, as if my thoughts were rays of sunlight, when I focused on them they dissipated immediately.

I told myself I would try again in a couple of days, but in my heart I knew it was no good. There was no way I could sit exams the following month. I closed my eyes and let out a long sigh. Proving myself had been a goal for a long time, yet lying in that hospital bed, cured of the ill health that had plagued me for so long, it didn't seem to matter.

Though I felt deeply the disappointment of having the opportunity to see what I could achieve taken away yet again, it was as if, during this long journey to find a cure, I had been purged of the feelings of failure for not doing well academically earlier in life. There were, after all, many other things more important. As I was analysing these thoughts, a tiny figure appeared by the bed.

'Hello. How are you today?'

It was the nurse who had helped to push me to theatre.

'Hello. I'm not too bad today, thank you. I haven't seen you around.'

'My days off.'

'Thanks ... for your kindness, just before they put me under,' I said.

'That's alright. I often hold hands around that time.'

'Oh.'

'It was actually very exciting. I've never seen anyone so blue when they came out of theatre before,' she said, sounding quite enthralled at the memory. 'The doctor gathered us around to show us your fingernails and explain what had happened, and then put the oxygen mask on you.'

'Glad to have been of some use.'

She smiled and we talked for a while before she went off to start her duties. There was a theatre list the following day and new patients began arriving late that morning, filling the beds that had been vacated earlier in the week. I hadn't got to know any of the men, not like on the traction ward.

Had I looked as nervous as these newcomers? Many of them came with wives, who made sure they were sorted out before leaving, promising to return in a few hours at visiting time. The new patients wandered in and out of the day room, picking up and putting down books and magazines, just as I had done.

Now I was one of the men who was no longer ill, but not quite recovered enough to be discharged. As I walked to the table for lunch, one or two glanced at the little plastic drainage bag with probably the same expression of apprehension that I had had on my first day.

I met the surgeon who had operated on me. He was pleased with my progress. It was the only time I ever saw him and I was sorry afterwards for not thanking him more for what he had done. Ann was a much more common sight on the ward.

Mr Goode visited that evening and I told him I couldn't sit the exams. He was very understanding and said not to worry about the HND as the college would award me the qualification based on my course work. During the week, several of the other students had come to see me and the main topic of conversation had been the enormous amounts of revision they were all doing.

On the Friday, I watched men being wheeled down to theatre. The porter was poking fun at a few people as they were leaving, and the tiny nurse sometimes holding hands before the little group had even left the ward. When the visitors entered that afternoon I saw the figure of Babs, clutching a bag that I guessed contained my washing, which she had been doing for me. Babs had been sitting by my bed for only a few minutes when she blurted out:

'There's been a terrible accident.'

I couldn't begin to guess what had happened and wondered if someone from the dance class had been injured. But before I had the chance to say anything, Babs delved into the carrier bag and produced a pair of child's pyjama bottoms, which she held up in the air. Was this a cryptic clue?

'Whose are those?' I asked totally mystified.

'They're yours. I thought it would be more hygienic to boil them ... but they've shrunk about four sizes!'

Staring at the garment I realised there were no clean pyjamas left. One pair was already in a bag, and I had planned to change during the visiting hour so that she could take away the ones currently being worn. Returning my gaze to Babs I saw the corner of her mouth quivering. I held out for only a few moments more before we burst out laughing.

On the Saturday morning one of the senior male nurses came to take out the drainage tube. I was lying in bed, reading. He pulled the curtains around and said that some of the other staff had not seen this done before, and they would come to watch.

He had only just spoken these words when two masked nurses appeared. They pulled down the bed clothes. Did I look stupid in those pyjamas! The top and bottoms refused to come anywhere near each other, while the latter stopped only a little below my knees. Two more arrived, also wearing masks.

I was beginning to think this must be a more complex procedure than I had imagined and when another two entered within the curtained area I was starting to feel slightly concerned. At least I couldn't tell if anyone was grinning at the sight of me. They all leaned over to watch as the charge nurse prepared himself for the task ahead.

I don't know what they were expecting, but removing the tube that ran from near the bottom of the operation site to the plastic drainage bag consisted of no more than giving it a good tug and then putting a large plaster over the hole. It was over quite quickly and they all left me to my book, although once they had gone several of the other men came over to ask what on earth had been going on behind the curtains.

Now that I was no longer attached to the bag, I was completely free to move around. The scar itched like mad, but the infection had been cured so there were no more javelin-throwing experiences, and I had no need for further painkillers.

On the Monday the old nurse who had given me the bed bath came to remove the stitches, which she did with a great deal more tenderness than when she had scrubbed my bollocks. It was two years to the day since I had first woken with a dull ache in the small of my back.

The next morning, Mrs Wilcox arrived to take me to Gammons Lane. She had brought the suitcase containing my day clothes so I went to the washroom to change. Shortly afterwards we left the hospital and made our way to the car park. It was beautiful outside.

Chapter Twenty-One

The commotion at the front door reached the point where I was forced to get up from my chair, step over the various bodies in my bedroom and walk to the top of the stairs. I already had a good idea of the cause. Another student had come to visit and Mr Wilcox, concerned at the number already in my room, was barring the newcomer from getting in. I shouted down that it was alright to send them up as we were only sitting around talking quietly.

I returned to the armchair and was followed into the room by Cathy, the only girl on the course. It was the evening after my discharge from hospital. The state of my health was only a passing topic of conversation as people were far more interested in the forthcoming exams, which would start in three weeks time.

They were revising every spare minute and I appreciated that so many had come to visit. I wouldn't see any of them again until the exams were over. In a way, I was envious because although they were working hard I didn't feel a part of the group any more, or anything else for that matter.

Like them, I should have been in the library each day, studying, worrying, frantically trying to understand at the last minute those odd subjects that had always been elusive to grasp. I should have been awake in my room until the early hours, my head filled with so many facts and figures it was ready to explode. My mind was instead virtually empty, unable to retain information for more than a few moments. In reality, my heart was no longer in it. They left about ten o'clock, amidst wishes of good luck on my side and a speedy recovery on theirs, Mr Wilcox counting them out at the front door.

I had to go back to the hospital approximately six weeks after being discharged to have another IVP, in order to find out how the kidney was reacting, now that the blockage had been removed. This meant I had to remain in Watford for the time being.

Mrs Wilcox was making my lunch each day, as well as my evening meal, which meant I didn't have to go foraging for fish and chips, or something similar. She had also kindly offered to do my washing, which saved me carrying clothes back and forward to the laundrette.

The weather turned hot and stayed that way, so each morning after a leisurely breakfast I made my way to the deck chair at the top of the garden. I was completely absolved of any responsibility; no studying, no daily chores, no reason to keep to any schedule. I drifted, dozing and daydreaming, with often nothing more to occupy my mind than watching a Red Admiral landing on a nearby flower.

It was certainly more pleasant to sit in the garden at Gammons Lane than to walk in the one that the hypno-therapist had been so keen to take me through. The only irritation was the scar and I was careful not to get too much sun on the itchy red line.

What surprised me was that I didn't think about the previous two years. Right up until the night before the operation I had analysed those months, studied the moves made, fretted over the various mistakes and the blind alleys followed. Yet now I didn't consider it at all.

Days blurred, flowing from one to another with nothing to differentiate them except the visitors who made their way to the patch of grass that had become my temporary place of residence. Most of them were from the dance class so they knew Mr and Mrs Wilcox, and as it was possible to walk up the side of the house to get into the back garden, they simply let themselves in.

I could hardly eat all the fruit that appeared. Someone even brought me a large slice of Bertha's bread-and-butter pudding, but I put this to one side until I had built up more strength to tackle it. My weight was increasing slowly and lying constantly in the sun was gradually giving me some colour again.

After about three weeks I regained sufficient enthusiasm and energy to consider trying to organise accommodation in Tonbridge, as my starting date with *Printing World* was still 8th August. I had kept the editor informed of my progress and he had been posting me copies of the local newspaper since I had come out of hospital. I made a few telephone calls to estate agents and landlords in the area, and agreed to travel down the following week to view a few properties that sounded promising.

It was quite an adventure to travel on the train from Watford into London and I made my way via Euston and Charing Cross to Tonbridge, arriving mid-morning. The publishing house was situated on the high street and I first went to the offices of *Printing World* to sort out some paper-work and have a meeting with Roy. He introduced me to the journalists who happened to be in the office, and I met the secretary, Phyll, again.

I was lucky with the accommodation and the first one I looked at, in nearby Southborough, was perfect. The house was currently being completely refurbished, but the owner assured me it would be ready for the beginning of August.

Cancelling the other visits I caught a train to London. Everything was finally coming together.

By the time I was due to go back to hospital for the second IVP I was well on the way to recovery, and had shaken off the apathy that had so overwhelmed me after the operation. The procedure was the same as on the previous occasion, with the sensation of heat rushing throughout my body when the radiographer inserted the needle disappearing within seconds. I was due to see the GP the following week for the results and, assuming there were no complications, I could then leave Watford whenever I wanted.

The exams were over by this point and although there had been one or two souls wandering around the college on the occasions when I had called in, the building had taken on that desolate emptiness, which educational establishments always manage to acquire so quickly at the end of term.

That coming Saturday, the people on the HND course were holding a party at one of the student's flats. By the Monday, almost everyone would have left the area, the majority going home, although there were a few who were starting jobs straight away and had new lives lined up in another part of the country.

As might be expected, there was a lot of drinking and a fair amount of letting off steam at the party. There were lads on the course from as far away as Japan and Nigeria, and we all knew we would never see them again. Feelings of joy, sadness, relief and apprehension were mixed up together for many of us. It was the end of an era. Whatever we did from that moment onwards, it was unlikely any of us would again be students.

The day after the party I began packing my belongings, although this wasn't exactly a big task and it didn't take long before the drawers and cupboards were empty and my bags full. I felt a twinge of disappointment while stacking the textbooks I wanted to keep, which had not been opened for a final rush of revision in the lead up to the exams. However, the moment was quickly gone. Despite everything, I had been happy at Gammons Lane.

On the Monday evening, I went to the dance class and for the last time I cast, spun, wheeled and arched (though fairly gently) with the dance group I had grown so fond of. I couldn't help the sadness that I felt at parting.

My appointment with the GP was early on the Wednesday and I had assumed there would be no complications, so had purchased a ticket to Newcastle for a train that left Kings Cross at nine o'clock the next morning.

As I sat in the waiting room I was glad that it would be the last time. The place held nothing except bad memories. I did not expect the results of the X-ray to show anything other than my kidney reducing in size, because there had not been a single attack since the operation. When I was finally sitting in front of the GP he confirmed that this was the case.

'Yes,' he said, looking at the results of the IVP, 'your kidney is getting smaller as we would expect it to.'

The last time we had faced each other I had been a wasted figure, stooped and shaking uncontrollably. Once more I praised the surgeon under my breath.

'Is there anything I need to do, or not do?' I asked.

'Just take it easy. It was a big operation and your body will not fully recover for many months, so treat it kindly.'

As I had been given the all-clear to leave the area, I felt that there could be no better start than to get away from the surgery. I didn't feel inclined to thank him for anything and he was obviously not going to make any comment unless it was to answer a question. We gave each other a curt nod and I was out the door.

I walked into Cassiobury Park. Everything was being done for the last time and I expected to miss my trips through the woods. The weather had been glorious for weeks. I was well-tanned and although still somewhat thin, looked quite healthy, which was rather ironic all things considered. I rested for a while on the bench where I had sat many times before and reflected quietly on the events of the last three years. I would never forget them. A new life waited for me in Kent. Exciting times were ahead and I was eager to move on.

I set off back to Gammons Lane to sort out some last-minute bits and pieces, so that I was ready for an early start the next morning. On arrival I noticed there was a letter for me, propped against the telephone just inside the front door. It was where Mr Wilcox always left my post, although I was mystified as to who had written on this occasion.

Upstairs, I sat at the small table and opened the envelope. The letter was from Mr Goode, who wished me the best of luck in my future career, and said I would always be welcome to call at the college. He was also writing to inform me that, based on the work I had done over the previous three years ... the college had awarded me the prize of best student on the course.

Author's Notes

Readers will see that the book is dedicated to my mother, who died of pancreatic cancer. Only about 3% of people with this cancer survive five years or more - a statistic that has barely improved in the last 40 years. The average life expectancy is just seven months from diagnosis.

Each year around 8,000 people in the UK are diagnosed with this condition. It has the highest death rate of all cancers. The Pancreatic Cancer Research Fund, PCRF, was formed in 2004 and provides a focus for fundraising to support more research into early detection and new treatments. Nearly £4m has been raised so far. More needs to be done and we can all play a part .... *www.pcrf.org.uk*

Author's Notes

Prologue

Spring 1946

That morning, the silence that had enveloped Camp 60 since the Italians left was shattered; destroyed violently, like the gates, as they were flung apart by a huge bulldozer. Hut after hut on the tiny Orkney island was torn down in a frantic race to erase all traces of war. As the work progressed, the demolition team moved ever nearer to the little chapel.

The contract was clear. Nothing was to be left.

Inside, the Madonna watched the entrance over the gates of Giuseppe Palumbi's rood screen ... and waited.

In the recreation hall, the three billiard tables that the Italian prisoners of war had made out of leftover concrete each had a neat triangle of balls set up for the next game. It had been eighteen months since the hut resounded with the ruckus of men laughing and cheering.

The screech of tearing metal was followed by brilliant daylight flooding across the tables, as the bulldozer ripped off part of the corrugated iron wall. The operator edged the machine forward, raised the bucket and brought it down sharply in the middle of the nearest table. It cracked cleanly in half and balls scattered across the floor to be crushed, returned to dust. Speed was everything; the destruction relentless.

The demolition crew started a fire just outside the camp, where the Italians had once burned the wood that could not

179

be used in the huts' pot-bellied stoves. Scenes of Italy, skilfully painted backdrops for plays and performances, were reduced to ashes. Domenico Chiocchetti's hard work was discarded, its value unrecognised.

While the flames raged and buildings crashed to the ground, the Madonna stared serenely. Eventually the door of the chapel opened, creaking in protest at being closed for so long.

Two men entered, wearing hats and overalls. Heavily built and tough, they were used to being obeyed without question. The immediate tranquillity took them totally by surprise. They walked along the nave, astonished at how realistic the imitation stone and brick walls appeared, until they stood before the rood screen.

The gaffer, an Irishman, placed his hands on the wrought-iron work, appreciating the skill required to turn scrap metal into an object of such delicate beauty. He wondered about the man who had dedicated so much effort to such a task.

Removing their hats, the two men entered the chancel to stare at the paintings of saints on the windows, angels and evangelists, the Madonna and Child above the altar. The gaffer picked up one of the brass candlesticks. He had spent more than thirty years putting up and taking down buildings, but had never been moved by one ... not like this. Something deep within him stirred and he wasn't sure why.

'What are you thinking, Pat?' asked the other man eventually.

His friend did not answer, the peace he had felt moments earlier eroded by waves of emotion; anger at the bureaucrat who had written the orders without checking what was on the site, fear that a different gang might have followed those orders, the chapel pulled down like a worthless hut.

'I'm thinking,' he said, barely controlling his feelings, 'that I'll not be the man who has to stand before God on Judgement Day and explain why I allowed such a dedication to His glory to be destroyed.'

'There's certainly some skill here, but you know what our contract says. The land restored to how it was before the war.'

'No, this is more than craftsmanship, Jack. Men put their souls into this and left a part of themselves behind.'

'There'll be a price to pay if we leave it.'

The Irishman replaced the candlestick so that the surrounding dust remained undisturbed.

'You know, this Nissen hut, *this* was the Italians' escape. They didn't dig a tunnel ... they built a chapel. It's a symbol.'

'Of what?'

'Hope. Tell the men, Jack, to leave the chapel and the statue. Make sure nobody misunderstands what I'm saying.'

'You're the boss.'

Alone in the building, the Irishman studied the paintings closely, poked his head into the vestry and then walked slowly back to the door, marvelling once more at the curved walls as he went. When he reached the entrance he looked back at the chancel.

'Made out of scraps,' he said, closing the door quietly behind him.

Back in the open, the pace of work was frantic. Wooden purlins were hurled on to the fire, while machines and men competed to eradicate what had been home for more than 500 Italians. There was no pretence to finesse; speed was the aim. A few men stopped briefly to look at the statue of St George slaying the dragon, just outside the impressive facade of the chapel, but neither was touched.

By the end of the day it was over. The huts were demolished. All that was left were the concrete foundations. A couple of men stacked the fence posts and made neat rolls of barbed wire for the landowner or local farmer to use. Anything else that could not be burned had been loaded on to the back of trucks.

The noise and activity stopped just as suddenly as it had burst upon the camp that morning and the chapel was alone again, still and silent.

This time there was no fence to keep people out.

Chapter One

January 1942

The Madonna's face swayed. Domenico Chiocchetti held the image in his hands as he sat in the bowels of a packet steamer, which had left Aberdeen that afternoon. The constant left-right motion was interspersed with a twisting action as the ship not only rode the waves but yawed from side to side. The rancid smell of vomit, unwashed bodies and cigarette smoke hung in the air alongside anger and despair, loneliness and dread. Domenico looked down at the picture and thought of his family and home ... and Maria.

He was thirty-one. A quiet, kindly, humble man. An artist, caught up in a war just like the other 1,200 Italian prisoners of war, captured during the North African campaigns, now being transported to some unknown destination. There was a rumour they were going to an island north of Scotland, but few believed such a place existed. Even if they had been told its name, it is doubtful any of the Italians would have heard of the tiny Orkney island of Lamb Holm. He had no idea his life would be bound to that island and to the image in his hands.

As he looked at the picture of the Madonna and Child, men around him murmured, coughed and retched. One or two wept in silence and several prayed because the journey was as terrifying as the battlefield. They felt helpless, at the mercy of the British army and the violent waters of the Pentland Firth. If the latter didn't sink them, which seemed increasingly likely, there was a good chance that a German U-boat might.

'Hey, Domenico. What's that card you're looking at? Domenico!'

Domenico looked up. He wasn't smiling, his mind still in his home village of Moena, where life had been simple, safe and wholesome. He stared blankly at Aldo; the easy-going, happy-go-lucky wheeler-dealer, whose cheeky grin made him look about sixteen. But Domenico sensed the vulnerability in the younger man. He thought the real Aldo Tolino was yet to be revealed to the world.

'You've been gazing at that card all the way from Liverpool.'

Domenico's face cracked into a smile.

'Since Durban before that, Egypt before that and Libya before that,' he replied, handing over the card.

Sergeant Giovanni Pennisi had been sitting with his eyes closed in an attempt, not to sleep, but to ignore what was going on around him. He looked down with eyes that were only half open and spoke for the first time since the ship left Aberdeen.

'It's one of a series of paintings of the Madonna and Child by Nicolo Barabino.'

'You know paintings, Sergeant Pennisi?' said Aldo, surprised both at being spoken to and the content of the comment.

'That's because,' said Domenico,' Sergeant Pennisi is a man of culture, a man of significant artistic talent. Something of which I suspect you, young Aldo, know little.'

Domenico and Pennisi shared a common bond in their burning desire to paint, but few of the other men knew of this or their friendship.

'Hey, I admit my talents lie elsewhere, but why do you treasure this card so much?' Aldo persisted.

Pennisi opened his eyes fully out of respect for his friend, who was about to speak of something close to his heart.

'My mother gave it to me just before I left. Sometimes I feel if I look at the picture, I don't have to look at the horror around me. It gives me strength at moments when the future looks bleak. And it reminds me of my mother.'

Aldo was not untouched by the honest explanation.

'It's beautiful,' he said. 'You can show it to her again when you return to Italy.'

Domenico laid the prayer card carefully in an empty tobacco tin and pressed the lid tightly closed, before tucking the tin safely into an inside pocket of his jacket. It was almost a ritual.

'At least for us the war is over,' said Aldo.

'There will be other things to fight Aldo,' answered Domenico. 'Boredom, loneliness, loss of hope ...'

The ship listed heavily and men grabbed frantically at what they could, including those next to them. The tension in the air vied with the smoke for space. With an agonising effort the ship gradually straightened and 1,200 Italians let out their breath.

'Someone said we're being sent to an island off an island and that it's so small if you turn around suddenly you will knock someone else into the sea,' said Aldo. 'The British must really fear that we are going to escape to send us to such a remote area ... like that place in America. What's it called?'

'Alcatraz,' said Pennisi, now committed to the conversation.

'That's it. They're sending us to Alcatraz,' said Aldo, his

185

boyish enthusiasm making him sound almost excited at the prospect.

'I think the British must have some purpose in mind to transport us to this remote island. I don't believe it's because they're worried that a few hundred weary Italian prisoners of war will escape en masse and overthrow their country,' said Pennisi.

A figure rushed past them to stop several yards away where the man was sick into a fire bucket. Pennisi closed his eyes. Aldo looked on with fascinated disgust.

'Wherever we're going we'd better get there soon,' he said. 'If there's a fire we'll be throwing vomit instead of sand.'

Pennisi replied without opening his eyes.

'Ah, but good Italian vomit,' he said.

Reproduced from Philip Paris's historical fiction, The Italian Chapel, published in 2009 by Black & White Publishing, Edinburgh. The Italian Chapel is available in hardback, paperback, large print, audio and ebook.

* * *

For nearly 30 years Philip Paris has worked in journalism and public relations within the graphic arts industry. Following the operation in 1983 the problem with his kidney never returned. Today, he lives in the Highlands of Scotland with his wife, Catherine ... a GP.

www.philipparis.co.uk